"TREEHEADS TOGETHER"

A true life fairy adventure from Aberfoyle

Adie Bain

First published 2011

Revised edition 2015

First edition published by Adrian Bain in 2011

Second revised edition published by Adrian Bain in 2015

Copyright © Adrian Bain 2011 2015

All rights reserved. No part of this publication may be reproduced, stored in a retrieval system or transmitted in any form or by any means, electronic, mechanical, photocopying, recording or otherwise without the prior permission of the copyright owner: The author and subsequent copyright owner is Adrian Bain.

Printed in Scotland by Airdrie Print Services Ltd

24-26 Flowerhill Street

Airdrie

North Lanarkshire ML6 6BH

Tel: 01236 751461

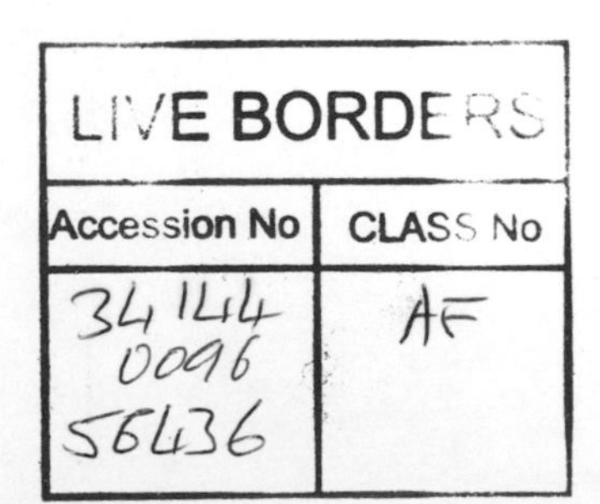

LIVE BORDERS

“Treeheads Together”: Table of Contents

CH2 Back with the strawberries: We find out from our previous visit what the fairies' favourite fruit is and head up to Aberfoyle with a few cartons as a gift. This chapter is a record of our adventures with the fairies on that day as seen through the eyes of Clara: Her visions, amazingly, correspond very closely to Robert Kirk's own written records. We had previously forbidden Clara to read these records for obvious reasons.

CH3 Aberfoyle; it's all "Doonhill" from here: Further adventures in fairyland.

CH4 Is it a frog? Is it a chimp? No; it's a goblin: Clara freaks out when she sees this ugly little creature in the woods. However, after establishing communication with the creature, Clara finds out he's a goblin called Grozwald who wants to get to know us better- and then the hilarity begins.

CH5 Grozwald isn't ugly; he's windswept and fun: Further adventures with this extremely ugly but very comical goblin.

CH6 Grozwald's babies: Grozwald introduces us to his wife and 3 young babies: Another hilarious encounter with the cheekiest goblin in Scotland.

CH7 Elves say prayers too; you know: "The Treeheads" arrive in Aberfoyle once more; blissfully unaware that it's prayer day for the elves. Clara describes the beautiful sounds of the worshipping elves.

CH8 "Salamander Day": The "Fire Spirits" are very explosive in Aberfoyle today and almost bring about the complete destruction of "The Treeheads".

CH9 Walking the right path: Clara and I stumble upon the "original path" up to "Fairy Hill" quite by accident- or was it by design?

CH10 "The Creatures of the Dark": "The Treeheads" arrive in Aberfoyle at dusk and a rather worried Grozwald warns us about "The Creatures of the Dark": Grozwald's warnings are not entirely unfounded; as we later find out.

CH11 "Sliding Plates": The ice is thick and extremely treacherous in Aberfoyle today. The other "Treeheads" laugh uncontrollably as they watch me slide downhill in my badly chosen footwear, but Clara later describes a vision which isn't quite as funny!

CH12 Aberfoyle can be a "pain in the neck": Clara and Lucy begin experiencing "phantom pains" on today's trip to Aberfoyle.

CH13 Alone and Misunderstood: Lucy and I are really down in the dumps today. Could we be subconsciously tapping into the feelings of Robert Kirk?

CH14 FREEDOM: Today is "WESAK"; the traditional festival of Buddhists all over the world. The elves had previously asked us to visit today, several months ago- but why? We are soon to find out on a truly amazing day that culminates in a completely unexpected climax to our wonderful adventures in fairyland, Aberfoyle.

Visions and Impressions: Clara "visits" Aberfoyle during Robert Kirk's lifetime and describes the place as it looked then. Clara then "tunes into" Robert, and gives us a valuable glimpse of the life of this very special man.

Latest developments: A lot has happened since 2009 (When our adventures in fairyland began): I have more evidence of the fairies' existence: I have seen Grozwald myself since then, and have reproduced a photo of "Thorak" (Grozwald's unfriendly cousin) on the back cover of the book to show everyone; which I hope is of interest.

ACKNOWLEDGEMENTS

There are so many people I'd like to thank so forgive me if I've missed anyone out:

Firstly, I'd like to give a big warm thank you to Collette O'Sullivan and Rosalie Nish for the front cover artwork. Next, I'd like to express my gratitude to Steven, Peter, and Olivier for their invaluable technical support.

May I also take the opportunity of expressing my sincere appreciation to Edinburgh University Library for allowing me access to Robert Kirk's original manuscript: I was extremely surprised to be granted the privilege of handling Robert Kirk's own personal book which is hundreds of years old!

Finally, I'd like everyone to give a GIGANTIC round of applause for The Reverend Robert Kirk; who had the courage and honesty to record his communications with the fairies of Aberfoyle, despite severe criticism from his peers. I hold you in high regard Robert.

I'd like to dedicate this book to the memory of "Big Geordie".

PREFACE

One afternoon, I was sitting in my old flat in Graham's road, Falkirk, when I got a frantic phone call from a friend I'd known for several years:

"Adrian, you'll have to visit Aberfoyle with me soon; I've been summoned up there by the fairies!"

I kept an open-mind and accompanied Lucy up to this sleepy wee village in Stirlingshire, Scotland.

I'd visited Aberfoyle before but was unaware of the fairy connection. It was only when Lucy told me about the legend of Robert Kirk and the fairies that I realized there was more to this place than I'd previously thought.

After listening to Lucy's fascinating story in a café in Aberfoyle, she showed me a book she'd bought about the legend of Robert Kirk and the fairies. I asked Lucy if I could borrow the book and she gladly let me have it.

Once back in my old flat in Falkirk, I avidly read the book and contacted Lucy a few days later with a brainwave I'd had: I suggested inviting along Clara to Aberfoyle sometime. After explaining to Lucy that my friend Clara was a "sensitive" (someone who can see phenomena that's invisible to most of the population); Lucy agreed.

I had absolutely no idea what we were all about to stumble upon.

Please read on...

INTRODUCTION

Hi everyone, we are "The Treeheads".

"What is a "Treehead"?" I hear you all asking. Well the answer would have to be ALL OF US! We are all totally dependent on the natural world around us for our very survival so; essentially, we are all "Treeheads". However, to save complicating matters too much, I'll give you a brief introduction to the "Treeheads" responsible for this book:

My name is Adrian and I work as a Staff Nurse in central Scotland. I have always been interested in alternative health and this has brought me into contact with many interesting people over the years.

I'll now move on to the two girls. Unfortunately, I can't give you their real names because they both wish to remain out of the spotlight for different reasons:

Let's start with "Lucy Lavender"(pseudonym). Lucy is a complimentary therapist and has earned her living in this area for many years. In fact, we met each other when we were both undertaking an alternative therapy course together many years ago. I can't give you any more information on Lucy because she wishes to stay well out of the spotlight.

Now on to "Clara Luckie"(pseudonym); whom I've deliberately saved to the last. All I can say about Clara is that her amazing visions of the otherwise hidden world around us is essentially what this book's about: Clara claims to possess the same abilities as the ancient Druids claimed to have: She tells me she can communicate directly with nature- and I believe her. In fact, I'd go as far as to say she's the most fascinating person I've ever met. What is probably a blessing in disguise is that, on the face of it, Clara is a very humble person who seeks neither fame nor notoriety; which is probably the reason she's been blessed with this wonderful gift in the first place.

I hope that I've given you enough introductory stuff for now because, quite frankly, what is to follow I'm sure will fascinate you as much as it did me. All I have done here is to record Clara's fascinating visions as they happened in fairyland, Aberfoyle, between 2009/2010 and, I'll tell you this; there were times when all three of us sensed or saw things that we couldn't explain, in the rational sense of the word. Before I finish here, I can promise you readers that I HAVE NOT altered any of Clara's "visions" or "communications" in any way, shape, or form.

I think I've said enough. Please read on, believe or disbelieve; the choice is yours, but above all else, at the very least, share in a wee giggle. Honestly, I couldn't have made this up even if I'd wanted to.

Kind regards,

Adie Bain

The Reverend Robert Kirk

Robert Kirk was a Presbyterian minister from the 17th century. He lived in the picturesque village of Aberfoyle, near Stirling.

Robert was not your average run of the mill minister, however- quite the contrary. He claimed to speak with fairies, and even had the audacity to write about his experiences, which have been reprinted in several books over the years.

Whether you choose to believe in fairies or not, Robert's life is a very poignant tale of a man of fine principles, caught between two worlds; the fairy and ours.

It was Lucy who first introduced me to the legend of Robert Kirk and I was immediately intrigued by the fact he was a "man of the cloth"!

He truly was a 17th century renegade and no doubt created quite a stir in his time. I'll give you a brief summary of his short but fascinating life:

Robert Kirk was born in Aberfoyle (Scotland) on the 9th of December, 1644. He was reputedly born "the seventh son of the seventh son"; which supposedly endowed him with the gift of "second-sight": This gift certainly seemed to apply to Robert as he claimed to be able to communicate with the unseen world of elves and fairies. Robert describes in his fascinating written records how he made regular trips up to "Fairy Hill" in Aberfoyle and, on one such visit, found himself in an underground cavern larger than Aberfoyle itself where he met some fairy folk whom he found friendlier and more congenial than humans (Does that surprise you?)

Robert, subsequently, began to spend more and more time with the elves and fairies, much to the consternation of his second wife who was at home alone; pregnant with their son Colin.

In his alleged written records, Robert describes how he meddles in the affairs of the fairies, with good intentions, but with dire consequences! He is subsequently imprisoned in the world of fairy, but not because he eats the forbidden fairy food which he said he had tasted and survived unscathed; but for his well-intentioned but misdirected involvement in the private affairs of the elves. (According to literature on fairies and folklore, humans are forbidden from eating fairy food: If a human indulges in any delicious offerings from the fairies, he or she can become trapped in fairyland forever! Robert seemed to prove this old superstition wrong when he supposedly enjoyed delicious banquets with the elves and, seemingly, escaped any consequence.

Having said that he also, according to legend, ultimately became trapped in fairyland anyway- SO BEWARE!)

In Robert's alleged writings, however, the elves do show him some leniency and allow him one last visit to his parish where he writes a final, no doubt tear-soaked letter to his beloved pregnant wife. On that very same day Robert's body is found on the top of "Fairy Hill", his life tragically cut short, without the chance to prove himself. (Legend has it that the body found on "Fairy Hill" was a "Doppelganger"; a German word meaning a "double", supposedly left there by the fairies to fool everyone while the REAL Robert Kirk was spirited away to fairyland- who knows? That secret still remains with the fairies and Robert I suppose.)

Before we continue with our fairy adventure, I would like to point out that Robert Kirk was not your average "head in the clouds" type of person- quite the contrary: He was credited as being the first person to translate the entire Bible from Latin into Scots/Irish Gaelic; which is no mean feat!

Now it's time to return to the fairies: Lucy showed me a copy of the book about Robert Kirk and his supposed adventures in fairyland. After reading his wonderful writings I thought if anyone could vindicate Robert's claims, Clara could. I'd known Clara for several years, and, as she slowly began to gain confidence in me, she began sharing her amazing visions of the unseen world around us.

Clara's stories absolutely fascinated me, and I felt that this poor man Robert Kirk deserved a break: He had probably been the subject of ridicule and mockery throughout his short but magical life.

I now had the opportunity of inviting Clara up to Aberfoyle to see if Robert was genuine with his fantastic claims- or not.

The adventure begins...

CH1 "The Treeheads" check out Aberfoyle 06.08.09

Lucy sounded very excited as she described an amazing set of coincidences that had guided her to Aberfoyle; and, ultimately, to the legend of Robert Kirk.

"Do you think fairies really exist?" Lucy blurted out excitedly.

Trying not to quell her enthusiasm, but at the same time wishing to ground her, I chose my words carefully:

"Look Lucy," I replied, "you know I'm one of the most open-minded people you'll ever meet; and I'm prepared to accept the possibility of numerous life forms we don't yet know about, but you have to be careful when talking about fairies: remember the old saying; "away with the fairies"!"

"Yes I know," Lucy replied impatiently, "but have you read Robert Kirk's book about the elves and fairies of Aberfoyle?"

"No, to be honest, I've never really been interested in fairies," I replied. "I always associated them with silly stories my mother used to read me before bedtime, desperate to get me to sleep so she could return to "The Sweeney"; a seventies cop show she loved at the time."

"You have to read Robert Kirk's writings," Lucy enthused. "They reduced me to tears."

"Okay then Lucy; lend me the book. I'll have a wee read and get it back to you as soon as I can," I conceded; always prepared to give someone the benefit of the doubt. So, to cut a long story short, I got Lucy's book about Robert Kirk's elves and fairies of Aberfoyle, read it and re-read it. To be truthful, if the book had been penned by anyone other than a 17th century church minister I might have confined it to the realms of pure fantasy; but a church minister in those days was taking a very big risk talking about such matters. Remember; this was only just over 50 years after "The Witch Trials" had ended!

So if this 17th century minister, Robert Kirk, was the "card-carrying" Christian he claimed to be, I knew just the person who could give this poor man a well-deserved break. Please read on...

"I'll tell you what Lucy!" I blurted out, possibly a wee bit prematurely. "I know this fantastic "sensitive"; she's the best I've ever met! Why don't we invite her up to this Aberfoyle place and let her check it out? If there are any "little green women" up there; she'll find them- I'm sure of it!"

"Okay then, we'll do it!" Lucy agreed in a defiant tone, visibly irritated by my flippancy, but keen to be proven right and not relegated to the lunatic fringe.

So the following day I telephoned Clara with an excuse to buy her a coffee and a snack in Falkirk, where I lived at the time. Clara accepted my invitation and drove through later, seemingly pleased at the invite; a chance to trawl round some different shops for a change. After a couple of sips of coffee and a bite of bun I made my move:

"Clara, can I share something with you?" I asked.

"What is it?" Clara counter-questioned, appearing slightly reticent.

"There's nothing to worry about, it's okay. I'm not going to ask you for money or anything. I just wondered if you fancied a trip up to Aberfoyle sometime?"

"What's up there like?" she quizzed.

"Well, I have this friend, she's an alternative therapist, and she loves Aberfoyle: It's a beautiful place in the middle of rolling hills and woodland... oh... and there's a lovely café that does home baking."

"Sounds nice, let's go sometime," Clara replied, her guard visibly lowered, and with an appreciative smile on her face.

So this was essentially it: The birth of "The Treeheads"

It was on a warm cloudless day that Clara and I arrived in Aberfoyle. She parked her car in the large car park next to the river. We were greeted by a pleasant cool breeze as we exited the car. I sent Lucy a text confirming our arrival and she sent one immediately back, telling me she was in the café across the road.

"Hi Lucy, this is my friend Clara, I so wanted you both to meet," I smiled.

As their eyes met there seemed to be an instant rapport which put me at ease. I then quickly took orders from them both for hot chocolate and cakes. There was something special about these two girls; I just instinctively knew it. They both seemed so happy in such a picturesque place and it wasn't long before they were chatting like old school friends. Lucy didn't mention anything about fairies at all to begin with; she was very discreet, as I had secretly hoped she would be:

"It's a beautiful day out there and we're in such a gorgeous place. Anyone fancy a stroll to work off that chocolate and banana cake?" suggested an animated Lucy.

I knew Clara wasn't a fan of walking great distances, and I could see by the expression on her face that she wasn't in the mood at the time, but she was too polite to decline. Once we were outside the sun beat down directly overhead but a pleasant cool breeze gently blew, taking the edge off the heat. We set off back towards the car park, following Lucy who was bounding ahead of us both.

"Could you slow down a wee bit Lucy?" I shouted. "Clara's wee legs aren't used to this kind of punishment."

We reached an old hump-backed bridge that looked like it was centuries old; just wide enough to get one car through. The river flowed gently below and the trees were like guards on duty; each one standing on its own water-eroded clump of earth. Once over the bridge we were faced with open countryside, slightly marred by a modern housing scheme on our right, but hey, it was a gloriously sunny day and it seemed a gentle enough stroll. I turned around to check on Clara, who was trailing behind me, and was so relieved to see an air of tranquility about her face which spoke volumes.

Once past the housing scheme, the houses became very sparse and I could see what looked like an old graveyard looming in the distance. To my surprise, Lucy entered the graveyard and I heard the screech of metal on metal as she opened the rusty old gates. Clara and I reluctantly followed her. With no disrespect to the dear souls who were interred there; it was a bleak looking place, visibly devoid of flowers and wreaths. Having said that, a lot of the gravestones were centuries old and had probably lain there for years, forgotten in the mists of time.

"What brings you in here?" I asked Lucy politely, but with an underlying tone of slight discomfort.

"Don't you know who's buried here?" she replied, visibly surprised by my ignorance. "It's the burial place of the famous Presbyterian minister, Robert Kirk."

"Who was he?" Clara asked innocently.

"He was the man who claimed to have met and lived with the fairy peop..."(Lucy was interrupted by Clara's sudden groans).

"What's wrong Clara?" we both enquired; visibly concerned by her discomfort.

"I... I think I'm okay; just got sudden pains in my chest," she

replied. "I'm just sensitive to old places like this."

"Robert died suddenly on the top of "Fairy Hill", didn't he?" I enquired; remembering having read it somewhere. "Maybe you're sensitive to the pain he felt just before he died?" I guessed; knowing that some "sensitive" people can feel the same pain of another just before their death.

Lucy nodded in agreement.

So we all walked over to the burial site of the famous Robert Kirk; and it certainly was an impressive gravestone, neatly inscribed in writing which appeared to be Latin; an ancient and dead language spoken by The Romans.

My knowledge of Latin was extremely limited but I stood there in the sunshine scrutinizing every word, searching for a similar word in English to try to make some sense out of it all.

I then turned to face the girls, hoping that they understood more than me, but they seemed as confused as I was.

I've reproduced the words on the following page to see if any of you readers understand them:

HIC SEPULTUS

ILLE EVANGELI

PROMULGATOR

ACCURATUS

ET

LINGUAE HIBERNAE

LUMEN

M. ROBERTUS KIRK

ABERFOILE PASTOR

OBIT 21 JUNE 1692

AETAT 48

However, I just felt generally uneasy in this desolate place. I've never liked graveyards at the best of times: the thought of all that rotting flesh and bones lying just below your feet; maybe some black-death virus lying dormant somewhere- who knows? Standing next to Robert's Gravestone, Clara began rattling off her impressions:

"I can feel a very strong energy here and I can see waves of clear light emanating from Robert's Grave," she explained.

Lucy looked askance at Clara; as if to say, "That's a good gypsy impersonation but I don't know if I'm buying it."

After leaving the graveyard, Lucy suddenly began belching repeatedly. Clara appeared quite embarrassed by the rude noises Lucy was making and I couldn't help but chuckle silently at the expression on Clara's face.

"Excuse... burp... me," explained a red faced Lucy, "this... burp... buurrp... happens to me every time I walk up this path. I must... buuuuurrrp... be sensitive to the energies around here."

Lucy's belching, thankfully, began to subside and finally Clara felt able to ask a question... *"Where are we going?"* she asked, looking intrigued but somewhat fatigued by the journey.

"It's a surprise," replied Lucy.

So we continued on our journey, passing an old cottage on our right which looked as if it had been there since Robert was alive in the 17th century. Eventually we came to a sign which read "The Fairy Trail". It was then Lucy began to "show her hand"; so to speak:

"Okay folks, I suppose I'd better explain why I brought you both here," and she began...

"Robert Kirk was a 17th century church minister who used to walk this path every day, and the legendary "Fairy Hill" is where he claimed to have met and spoken to the fairy people. I initially invited Adrian to join me on my trip up here alone but he suggested I bring you here as well Clara. He told me about your abilities and said if there was anything to see then you would see it! I apologize for the secrecy but Adrian was worried that if I told you beforehand then you might not have come."

"He was probably right: I wouldn't have come!" Clara replied sternly; giving me a look that would have turned "The Gorgon" into stone. *"But I suppose I'm here, so I don't want to disappoint anyone."* (I made a motion to pat Clara on the back as an

apologetic gesture but she just shrugged me off. No more coffees with Clara for a while, I thought.)

So we entered the woodland that signaled the start of "The Fairy Trail" and Lucy darted away ahead of us both; negotiating the steep incline on the path with relative ease.

As for poor Clara; she puffed and panted away in the distance but waved me on when I offered to backtrack and give her some moral support.

As I negotiated the steady incline, I couldn't help but feel that the surrounding woodland did seem to have a "Brothers Grimm" type atmosphere to it! This truly was an enchanting place: the trees were close together; shading us from the strong sun, and there was a dark green dappled look to the surrounding vegetation. Lots of hiding places for "The Little People", I thought excitedly- if they really do exist?

Looking ahead, I could see the path meandering upwards with Lucy appearing as a tiny speck; away in the distance.

I eventually arrived on the top of "Fairy Hill" in second place, behind the energetic Lucy. To be honest, I was disappointed at the sight that met my eyes. I don't know what I was expecting to see;

maybe a cottage made out of candy with a sugar-icing roof, I don't know. Instead, I was greeted by three rather gnarled old trees; each one decorated with multi-coloured ribbons and scarves, and surrounded by fairy ornaments. On closer inspection, however, my initial disappointment turned to pity as I read some of the heart-wrenching wishes that some of the believers had left pinned to the tree trunks.

There were also coins of different currencies wedged into the gaps between the bark; indicating that there were believers from all over the world making pilgrimages to this place. Feeling obliged to make a wish too, but also being Scottish, and careful with my money, I pushed a *brand new penny* into the bark of "Fairy Tree" and made my wish. To be honest, I still found it hard to believe in the fairy folk, and the fairy ornaments around the tree certainly didn't strengthen their case. Once Clara recovered her puff, however, my curiosity was instantly reignited...

"On the journey up here, I suddenly got a vision of myself dressed in a monk's brown habit: I get the feeling that this place has been visited for centuries by many religious orders," she said.

Clara then began wandering around "Fairy Tree", trying to pick up information. Stopping just to the right of its gnarled trunk, she began reciting her impressions:

"I can feel a strong energy vortex here... oooh... it's so strong... it feels as if it's trying to pull me downwards!" With that, she quickly moved away from that spot. Then, without warning, 3 black beetles wandered out from "Fairy Tree" towards us. It was difficult to tell exactly where they came from, they just seemed to appear...

"Beetles are very special creatures," Clara announced, as if she was receiving information from somewhere. *"They act as "listening-posts"; and return underground with any information gathered."*

Well they certainly didn't look very special to me! My immediate impulse was to squish them into the ground with my size elevens. But if this fairy stuff was really true, I didn't want to get off on the "wrong foot"; so to speak.

Clara then laid her hands on "Fairy Tree", with both feet in contact with its roots, and closed her eyes in deep concentration. Her visions continued:

"This tree is a very special tree and is protected by a golden light which surrounds it like a force-field."

I sat listening intently to Clara with every faith that what she was describing she was actually seeing- but Lucy still appeared incredulous.

"I feel a degree of suspicion from the beings that inhabit this place," announced Clara.

What do you mean by beings? What beings? What do they look like?" Lucy quizzed; with a distinct air of skepticism.

"How can I tell you what they look like if they won't show themselves," Clara replied, in a firm but polite tone.

I decided to interject with my own diplomatic contribution:

"Look fairy folk, if you really exist, as Robert Kirk said you did, please show yourselves- we mean you no harm." Barely had I got the sentence out when I heard voices in the distance. Unfortunately though, it wasn't a troop of "The Little People" out hunting with their miniscule bows and arrows, as Robert Kirk described in his writings, but a young family with two pretty wee daughters. The mother carried a red box in her arms containing candles and other gifts for the fairies. She seemed to take the whole thing very seriously. Poor dad, however, looked as if he was just along to keep the peace. We watched intently as the innocence of the wee girls seemed to charge the atmosphere with much needed energy: They were a joy to watch and mum seemed very much a believer; giving very precise directions to the girls as they proceeded to lay their gifts around "Fairy Tree". Once everything was laid out, mum lit some candles and the girls made wishes to the fairies; their cute wee voices a joy to the ear, and the innocence of their sincerity extremely touching. I could feel tears welling up in my eyes; my *one-penny offering* suddenly returning to haunt me!

Then the wee girls left with Mum and Dad and we were suddenly alone again- or were we? Even I could feel a distinct change in the atmosphere; so what was the amazing Clara picking up? She didn't disappoint:

"The appearance of the wee girls was too much for them; they couldn't contain themselves!" Clara suddenly blurted out in excitement, once the family were out of earshot.

"What did they look like?" I asked excitedly (Lucy still appeared unconvinced).

"Well the ones I saw I can only describe as appearing like very thin five year old children," Clara explained.

Marginally disappointed by her answer, I quizzed her again: "Ok then, what were they doing when the two girls were here?"

"They seemed to take sheer delight in the children's presence," Clara enthused. *"As the girls bent over to place their wishes at "Fairy Tree", I could see them placing their fairy hands over the children's heads: maybe they were blessing or healing them, I don't quite know."*

Unfortunately though, what Clara had seen didn't match up with Robert Kirk's descriptions, and Lucy didn't appear convinced at all.

So Lucy and I sat down with our backs to "Fairy Tree" and got out our lunchboxes. Clara was still standing though; too focused on her visions to be interested in eating- and she hadn't finished yet...

"I can see two elves behind you both just now; they each have one arm outstretched towards your backs, and their palms are facing upwards: I think they're checking your "auric fields"." (The "auric field" is supposed to be an energy field that surrounds every living organism and, up until recently, it could only be seen by "seers" such as Clara; but now fairly recent camera techniques

such as "Kirlian Photography" make it available for all to see- including me.)

Lucy started belching again as Clara began describing what she could see: *"The two elves are laughing at the noises you're making just now Lucy,"* Clara informed her.

"Burrp... Glad someone finds it funny," replied Lucy, now sounding slightly more convinced due to the timing of Clara's visions with her subsequent belching.

"That's them finished now: They're clapping their hands together in unison," continued Clara.

Lucy was now beginning to warm to Clara's visions, and was now sitting with an expression of child-like wonder on her face, listening intently to Clara's every utterance. Once her belching had subsided, Lucy produced a tangerine from her bag and began sharing it with us all- not forgetting the fairies of course!

I took a piece of tangerine and, finding it bitter to taste; screwed up my face like a freshly rinsed sock.

"The two elves were chuckling at the face you pulled when you bit into that piece of tangerine," Clara informed me.

Turning around quickly and addressing "thin-air", I quipped:

"Okay fairies, you lot have a taste and I wish I could see the look on your fairy faces!"

"One of them has just put his hand on a piece of the fruit that's on the plate. Now he's just picked it up and is starting to eat it. He hasn't screwed up his face like you just did," explained Clara.

"That's because he HASN'T had any! Look Lucy; both pieces of the fruit are still there for all to see," I retorted.

Lucy agreed: both pieces of tangerine were still lying, evidently untouched.

"Wait a minute!" insisted an indignant Clara: *"The piece of fruit that the elf ate WASN'T the physical piece that's left: What the elf ate was TRANSPARENT, and he seemed to "LIFT" it out of the physical piece with his hands."*

Lucy was visibly taken aback by Clara's latest statement as she was infatuated with the legend of Robert Kirk and had researched more heavily on fairies than I had: What Clara had just described coincided with stories Lucy had read about fairies taking the "ESSENCE" out of food without humans being aware.

Clara then began laughing again at what just seemed like an empty space; intriguing us both...

"What are you laughing at now Clara?" we both asked, amused by her sudden mirth.

"One of the elves is mocking the "generous" one-penny offering you made earlier Adrian," Clara replied; her eyes wet with tears.

"Ok then, share it: I can take it on the chin!" I replied, with a reluctant smile.

"He's standing in front of you just now rubbing his thumb and forefinger together, and wriggling his bottom to and fro, with an expression of sheer impudence on his face."

"I think you've said enough," I interrupted, slightly embarrassed.

Lucy and I leaned back against "Fairy Tree". We were both genuinely impressed by what Clara had seen but it seemed the fairy folk had kept their best until last...

""The Elf Queen" has just appeared before me!" exclaimed Clara with a transfixed stare.

"Describe what she looks like," Lucy and I both implored.

"Okay, she's a beautiful woman of human appearance with long dark blonde hair; gathered up above her majestic features, and she's wearing a silver head-piece adorned with a single jewel. Her

clothing is of a pearlescent hue, elegantly tailored, and gathered up at meticulously chosen points on her elegant figure; accentuating her stately appearance. She is gently smiling at me just now, which makes me feel very welcome."

With that, Clara curtsied. Then she returned to join us both.

Lucy and I turned to face each other. Our amazed expressions said it all. What a turnout for our first visit; nothing less than "Her Majesty Herself"! We all bowed together; deeply honoured that none other than "The Elf Queen" had decided to visit us on our first trip together.

"What can I bring them all as a gift next time?" I asked, directing my question towards Clara.

"They're telling me they like berries; and their children love strawberries," Clara replied on their behalf.

"Okay fairy folk: consider it done!" I replied with glee.

On our way back down "Fairy Hill", we bumped into a couple from Yorkshire out on a fairy pilgrimage. I stopped to talk with the couple briefly:

"The fairies' favourite food is berries; especially strawberries-honest it is," I smiled.

CH2 Back with the strawberries 12.08.09

Remembering to bring some strawberries with us, we headed back to Aberfoyle like excited school kids. Before you make any comments about my Scottish "generosity", I also brought melon and pineapple because I figured these delicacies would be unheard of in "their neck of the woods", so to speak.

As you can imagine, this was a totally new experience, at least for Lucy and I: the chance to interact with a race of beings that were, to all intent and purposes, invisible to the naked eye.

"Maybe I'm crazy," blurted out a self-doubting Clara, as she drove her wee car towards Aberfoyle. *"Maybe this is just my mind acting out some fantasy or something."*

"Look Clara!" I replied with an air of exasperation, "I have known you for at least five years and a lot of what you've seen I'd previously read about in books on the unexplained and, the other stuff... well... that just amazes me! Your visions on "Fairy Hill" had enough consistencies to tie in with Robert Kirk's claims, and you also saw other stuff which Robert didn't mention in his writings- that's good enough for me."

Lucy nodded emphatically in agreement: This "deeply-rooted" support from the other two "Treeheads" allowed Clara to visibly "blossom" before our very eyes: Her driving position almost instantly relaxed and the tension caused by self-doubt melted away; leaving an air of serenity on her face.

As we neared our destination, the clouds rolled by thick and fast above our heads and, intermittently, little spurts of drizzle would smear the car windscreen. The views from the car were soothing to the eye: meandering green fields framed by hills, dotted with trees and cattle, and the pencil grey sky added a sense of mystery and awe to the place.

"Please parking angel, give us a space," begged an excited Lucy as we drove into the quaint old village of Aberfoyle. Sure enough; the small car park was full as usual, but Lucy's prayer seemed to be answered as someone was reversing out of a space just as we were arriving. The two girls smiled at each other but my male logic told me it was just sheer luck. We all jumped out of Clara's car and, visibly charged with adrenaline; Lucy grabbed the picnic hamper clumsily from the back seat. The two girls rushed ahead and, following closely in the distance was I, pen and notebook at the ready; scribbling furiously as I walked.

I was hoping to give Robert Kirk's graveyard a miss but Lucy insisted on paying her respects again. I suppose this book would never have been written without him, so I reluctantly entered the cemetery; closely following the girls over the damp cold grass as they headed towards Robert's Grave. I really didn't like graveyards at the best of times but this place was as bleak as ever. There wasn't a flower in sight; and the ones Lucy had left on her last visit had somehow melted into the grey:

"The flowers I planted at Robert's Grave on Sunday have disappeared!" wailed Lucy.

Why is Lucy getting so emotional? I privately thought. She's behaving like this man is some sort of recently deceased relative or something. He's been dead longer than the Dodo! But, to my surprise, Clara embraced Lucy with a comforting hug.

Once outside the graveyard, Lucy burst into a tirade of belches again: "Burrrrrrrrrp... burp... sorry... burrrrrrrrp... goodness me... I can't stop.... burrrrp." This continued for quite some distance, almost up to the sign marking the start of "The Fairy Trail". Clara also complained of feeling nauseous but I felt fine; secretly relieved I wasn't sensitive enough to react to the energies in this place.

"I think it's this path: there's something about it that makes me belch uncontrollably," Lucy intuited.

"This path has been walked by many a holy man in the past," announced Clara. *"There are strong energies here, it's hard to explain,"* she continued. We stopped briefly to gather our strength and quench our thirsts, before we started our ascent towards "Fairy Tree".

Barely had we entered the woodland at the foot of "Fairy Hill" when Clara genuinely spooked me by shouting out in a loud squeaky voice: *"They're here-They're here!"*

"What do you mean by: "They're here-They're here"?" Lucy quizzed, visibly intrigued.

"The elves somehow knew we were coming even BEFORE we'd arrived: There seems to be an intricate communication link between the numerous life forms in this place; it's too complex for me to fathom," explained Clara.

I was beginning to wonder if the girls secretly wanted to turn me into a gibbering wreck when Lucy, suddenly, let out an ear-piercing shriek!

Visibly shaken, Clara and I turned round to face Lucy and were confronted by a woman contorted in pain, with tears streaming down her face: "I feel as if someone is pushing a knife slowly into my right side; I've never felt pain like this before- EVER!" sobbed Lucy.

Being a nurse by profession I had to discount anything medical, so I quickly took Lucy's wrist between finger and thumb; and counted her pulse rate. I was greatly relieved to feel steady, normal beats: "Your pulse is normal Lucy," I reassured her. "How do you feel? Do you want to go back to the car and we can phone a G.P.?" I suggested.

"No, I think it's something to do with this place," Lucy surmised. "I feel much better now- let's continue," she replied.

Then Clara began sharing a vision with us both; providing a possible answer for Lucy's sudden excruciating pain:

"The ghost of Robert Kirk is with you just now," she explained. *"He didn't mean to cause you this discomfort but he did die with a heart-attack; and this traumatic experience will still be imprinted on his "energy field"; so you will feel his pain. He feels drawn to you*

just now and is worried that your interests lie too much with the fairies; at his own expense." (There is no mention in any of the material I've read about Robert Kirk that suggests he died of a heart-attack but his body was apparently found slumped on the summit of "Fairy Hill" which does suggest a sudden, untimely death).

Back to the story...

"I can assure you Robert it was your moving book that brought me to this place, and it is you that I feel the connection with so, don't worry, I'm not neglecting you," Lucy announced in a reassuring tone.

"I can hear him now," Clara continued, *"He keeps saying: "I'm sorry- I'm sorry- I didn't mean to cause you any pain"."*

Lucy now appeared visibly comforted by Clara's vision: In fact, we were all relieved that Lucy's sudden discomfort seemed to be firmly "rooted" in the fairy realms. With that, we continued our hike up the wooded slope towards "Fairy Tree". When we eventually arrived at the top of "Fairy Hill" we were confronted by the sight of three young women sitting to the right of The Tree. Obviously, their presence inhibited our freedom to talk as openly as we would have liked, so we all sat down next to The Tree and exchanged pleasantries with the women.

"Do you believe in fairies?" I asked them.

"I believe there's something here," one of them replied. "There's too much of an atmosphere to this place- it's quite eerie in fact," she continued.

She then went on to point out that the trees seemed to have been deliberately planted in a circular fashion, with "Fairy Tree" at the centre. I pretended to be the "innocent tourist type" and nodded in agreement. Maybe these young women knew more than they were letting on, I thought- but I kept my feelings to myself. However, barely five minutes after we'd arrived, the young women all stood up to go. We said our goodbyes, secretly relieved that we now had the place to ourselves; and could be as "away with the fairies" as we pleased! We gave the young ladies a few minutes to disappear then, with a sigh of relief, we produced our lunchboxes; full of sandwiches, cakes, cartons of orange juice, and, of course, our gifts for the fairies. No sooner had we gotten our picnic out than we heard Clara addressing some invisible being who seemed to be standing close by:

"Yes, you can have some if you like," she said; talking to what seemed like just an empty space.

"Who was that you were talking to?" Lucy and I both whispered, worried in case the three young women might still be within earshot.

"It's one of those "wee thin ones"", Clara replied. *"He just popped his head round my shoulder and asked for some of my orange juice."*

"DON'T DRINK IT IF A FAIRY HAS TOUCHED IT!" I ordered; remembering that Robert Kirk had related an ancient superstition in his book about eating fairy food and becoming trapped in fairyland... FOREVER! Maybe I was being over-cautious, but Clara obeyed and poured the contents of her cup onto the ground. So we continued eating our picnic while talking quietly amongst ourselves, breathing the country air which was gently infused with the smell of the surrounding pine woodland. We hadn't long finished our meal, however, when Lucy began grimacing in genuine discomfort again. At this point I was becoming genuinely concerned that she might have some underlying medical condition when Clara instantly put my mind at ease:

"The ghost of Robert Kirk is close by you again Lucy. He seems to have a genuine fondness for you."

"Well, he's got a funny way of showing it: I'm in agony here!" Lucy groaned, but was still able to raise a smile of genuine affection for the deceased reverend. Lucy then appeared to recover fairly quickly and was informed by Clara that Robert had now left. Visibly relieved that Robert had now gone, despite his well-meaning intentions, Lucy was now bursting with energy and eager to make contact with the other invisible beings around us:

"Let's give them our fruit offering," she enthused; as she reached for the container that held the strawberries, melon, and pineapple. With that, Lucy ceremoniously cleaned a plate lying nearby which was decorated with fairy designs, and carefully placed on it pieces of strawberry, melon, and pineapple. She barely had time to lay the plate down when Clara continued the narrative:

"They can hardly wait: they've been eyeing up those strawberries for ages. Look at them!" she chuckled. *"They're arguing over the strawberries: it's hilarious to watch!"*

"Who are Clara? Remember, we can't see a thing- and what

about my melon and pineapple?" I reminded her. "That took me ages to prepare!"

"Sorry folks: I forget that it's only me who can see them. Okay- It's the "wee thin ones" that look like five year old children- and I'm afraid they're leaving the other fruit just now: it's the strawberries they're after... wait a minute... one of them has picked up some melon and is eating it, and another is away with a piece of pineapple," continued Clara.

The "wee thin five year olds" apparently made short work of the fruit as Clara informed us very shortly afterwards that it was all gone. However, looking at the plate; it was hard to believe that a bunch of "wee thin, invisible five year olds" had even had so much as a sniff, as everything was still lying there as before, apparently untouched. Having said that, I trusted Clara implicitly, and Lucy seemed to be warming to her abilities too.

"That's them bowing in thanks just now," Clara informed us both.

As a gesture of appreciation; Lucy and I both curtsied back and, with that, Clara informed us that the "elf kids" had now gone. Clara then put her right foot on one of the roots of "Fairy Tree"; attempting to establish contact with its "tree spirit": *"I can't detect the golden hue surrounding "Fairy Tree" like I did the last time: Its aura isn't as bright today.*"

Trusting that Clara had never read Robert Kirk's Writings, before or after coming to Aberfoyle, and also promising never so much as to look at a single word or picture; dare it tarnish her amazing visions, I was desperate to quiz her further:

"Okay then Clara, what can you pick up just now with regard to Robert Kirk and the fairies?"

"Well... I have a vision in my mind's eye of a young man with "second-sight" who becomes entangled in the fairy realms; and allows himself to become enchanted by them."

Lucy and I sat entranced; so far Clara was spot on, and there was more to follow:

"Wait, "Fairy Tree" is taking me down... down past its roots... down deep into the earth below." Shielding her eyes; as if protecting herself from a sudden glare of intense light, Clara paused for a moment before continuing:

"I am now in a vast underground cavern; so vast it could contain the whole of Aberfoyle itself- and much more!"

"What do you see, what do you see?" Lucy and I blurted out,

overcome with intense excitement.

"Wait a minute!" exclaimed Clara, *"You don't realise how difficult this is: my eyes are trying to focus just now... bear with me... ooh... that's fantastic! I can see vast cities stretching away into the distance. There are many caverns underneath this hill. The King and Queen of fairyland live in a big crystal cavern, and sit on two crystal thrones. The backs of the thrones finish in a point and are of a gothic style, brightly coloured, and shine from an unknown light source. Oh, she has arrived; The Elf Queen herself! She is bestowing her blessings upon us. Thank you most kindly Your Majesty."*

With that, Clara curtsied, and Lucy and I felt obliged to do the same; rising to our feet in a gesture of respect.

Then silence... We recovered our senses and, glancing at my watch, I realised we'd been sitting up here for well over an hour. Clara shared one final insight with us before we left:

"The elves told me that while we were up here they've been giving us healing."

"Well it doesn't feel like it!" I groaned. "I've got a pounding headache and I feel sick."

"Sometimes after a healing session the body releases toxins

which have been stored up for a while. I have noticed this in my practice and, like you say, the symptoms can present very much like a hangover: but this is a cleansing; it's a good thing. If it's any consolation Adrian, I feel much the same way you do. What about you Clara? How do you feel?" asked Lucy, diverting her gaze towards her.

"I'm… (yawn) just a wee bit cold and tired. I suppose a hot chocolate with marshmallows and cream would be most welcome just now," Clara replied; licking her lips at the thought.

"Well, I think we should take Robert Kirk's advice and give "The Elf Queen's Gourmet Cafe and Bistro" a miss and head back to the coffee shop in Aberfoyle," I joked.

We thanked the fairies and said our goodbyes. On our way back down "Fairy Hill", Clara swore she could hear a multitude of voices shouting goodbye- or could it just have been the gentle rustle of the surrounding trees?

A Meditation for the Children

Clara went home that evening to ponder over the wonderful visions she'd had that day, and the following morning she telephoned me; eager to share in her latest insights. So here they are, in Clara's own words:

"Suddenly, I was sitting at a table looking at a white book with "MY LIFE" printed on its cover in gold lettering. As I was flicking through the pages, I could see projections of previously important events in my life: It was like watching a movie. I eventually got to the present page; which was our trip together that day to Aberfoyle. As I was viewing the scenes before my eyes, I silently asked the fairies for proof of their existence: Almost instantly, a figure clad in green appeared, took me by the hand, and led me into a massive, brightly lit, underground cavern. I couldn't see the light source but the light looked like "rainbow light".

We were walking on what seemed like a glass floor; very highly polished- whether it was made of glass though, I can't be sure. At the end of this cavern there appeared two thrones; each made of crystal and carved in a gothic style.

I peered down at myself and noticed that I was clad in a wonderful gown which was deep violet in colour.

Suddenly, a spiral of purple/blue butterflies appeared up high. I held my hands outstretched and they landed on me. They were extremely uplifting and I silently stood gazing at them in sheer admiration.

The figure in green then pointed to a corridor; its floor was lined with rose-quartz and there was a winding path which snaked into the distance; intermittently broken up with tall pillars of crystal of varying colours: Beside each crystal pillar stood a tall being; each being matched the colour of the crystal pillar it was standing next to. All of these beings shone; emanating a bright light.

At the end of the corridor appeared a large "waterfall": On closer examination, I noticed the "waterfall" was actually made up of tiny crystals. I walked through them and they felt like tiny hailstones, clinging to my aura; cleansing and purifying me.

When I emerged on the other side, a gentle breeze blew the crystals off. I was then informed I had received a gentle cleansing from the fairies. I noticed my previously deep violet gown had changed colour; and was now radiant white, with a silver trim.

I stood there in deep gratitude, praying silently for all the innocent children in this world who were needlessly suffering: I don't know why but their sad plights seemed to be impressed on my thoughts at that moment."

(My words: Fairies are known; according to folklore, to adore young children.)

CH3 Aberfoyle: it's all "Doonhill" from here 19.08.09

This fairy thing was really beginning to take hold of me. Most people pop over to their local supermarket for a bottle of "fairy liquid", but how many of you folks would admit to going shopping for the fairies? Well, here goes, my neck is now firmly in the noose:

On the morning of the 19th of August, I trawled around my local shop looking for great strawberry offers, and sourced some Tayside grown strawberries at a reasonable price. They were plump, juicy, and made me proud to be Scottish. I hurried back to my flat in Falkirk, washed them, and plucked out their stalks. They came out with ease, indicating their ripeness. I was just in the process of dusting them with a generous helping of sugar when the phone rang. It was Clara:

"Where have you been? We were supposed to be meeting Lucy up in Aberfoyle at midday, It's now after eleven!" she exclaimed.

"Doesn't time fly?" I parroted; having been caught firmly on the hop.

Shortly afterwards, a hot and flustered Clara arrived at my door, visibly anxious that I'd made her late for our meeting with Lucy. However, Clara got her own back on me later as I was thrown about in her car like a pensioner on a bus fitted with air brakes, as she tried to make up for lost time.

"It's okay," I said, trying to reassure her, "Lucy is fine. She knows what I'm like. In fact, she almost expects me to be late." That didn't work either, however, and Clara eventually arrived in Aberfoyle, red faced and apologetic, even though we were only half an hour late.

Lucy, however, was cool, very cool. In fact, she was visibly beaming when we walked into the café and this instantly settled a visibly agitated Clara.

Feeling a certain responsibility to try to make amends, I treated everyone to our joint favourite hot chocolates, with marshmallows and cream, along with freshly baked scones and jam. This seemed to appease a hot and flustered Clara, and it wasn't long before she was pouring out the details of her recent meditation to an enthralled Lucy.

"I hope you're writing all this down Adrian," said Lucy, seriously addressing me, but with a glint of humour in her eyes.

"Of course I am, but I do wish sometimes that you folks had a wee bit of writing talent as well: my wrist is sore with all this constant typing!" I grumbled.

"Aw, diddums," both girls replied, and they both gave me a smile and a wink. We were just about to leave the café when, suddenly, the skies outside turned coal black: It was like the lights had suddenly been switched off! We had no option but to remain seated and watch the impending downpour... and a downpour it was! The rain pelted down in sheets, and soon the street outside looked more like a river. Eventually, the rain subsided but it continued to drizzle relentlessly all the same.

We sat for what seemed like an eternity, hoping for a break in the cloud cover, but it looked like the drizzle was here to stay. So, it was with a degree of reluctance that we exchanged the warm snug café for a water-logged journey back up to "The Fairy Trail".

So off we set, and as we were trudged over the hump-backed bridge again, torrents of water surged against the walls of this antique structure; and I wondered if it could cope with the sudden swell. The river below had swollen with the heavy downpour, and the trees were inundated in its frothy, dark waters. I was secretly relieved when the bridge was well behind me. The girls, however, seemed oblivious and were engrossed in deep conversation:

"I must pay my respects to Robert," insisted Lucy.

The drizzle was persistent and the wind was driving it into our faces, so, as you can imagine, I wasn't keen in visiting musty old graveyards but, going along with the overall consensus, I reluctantly followed the two girls into that forbidding place. Once inside the old cemetery, however, I didn't feel the same oppression as I had felt on our previous visits. Lucy mirrored my thoughts exactly:

"Can't you feel how still and peaceful it is in here today?" she commented.

Lucy appeared in her element; in this place full of old bones and stones: "Look!" she exclaimed: "Look at the "Scotch Mist" on the top of "Fairy Hill"."

Sure enough, "Fairy Hill" was surrounded in a ghostly mist which I found quite eerie. Fancy going to see a movie instead? I felt like saying- but didn't.

Lucy, taking the lead in this desolate place, began walking towards Robert's Grave, with Clara following closely behind her.

The grass underneath was saturated with this perpetual drizzle and felt like slimy seaweed underfoot. I stopped briefly to read a few inscriptions on the gravestones as I was passing, but this only served to dampen my spirits further. I eventually caught up with the girls, who were already standing beside Robert's grave when I arrived. I was relieved to see that Lucy's flowers from her last visit were still intact; although somewhat withered and shriveled. Visibly relieved that her offerings of respect had not been destroyed, she removed them; replacing them with a fresh, perfumed, and brightly-coloured bunch. Then, thankfully, we left together.

"Look, I'm not getting the belching- nor am I getting any stabbing pains," Lucy announced gleefully, once we'd exited the cemetery. No sooner were the words out of her mouth when her eyes began streaming with tears...

"My eyes, my eyes are stinging like mad!" she grimaced. "It feels like someone has sprayed them with soap!"

'Poor Lucy', I thought: She certainly gets her fair share of ailments.

"I think you're being prepared for the gift of "second-sight"

Lucy," announced Clara.

Understandably; Lucy didn't immediately react with rapture and applause, and shout out: "Great, I'll soon be able to see ghosts and goblins like you can Clara!" Instead, she continued to suffer in silence. Eventually though, Lucy's "second-sight hay fever" began to recede, and soon she was able to continue with us on our journey back up to "The Fairy Trail".

However, we were all finding it really hard going: the wind had changed direction and was blowing rain drizzle directly into our faces. Even with our waterproofs on we still felt cold and damp. We squelched past the old cottage on our right; its walls were stained dark grey with the steady, driving drizzle. The roof tiles were old, probably nail sick, and the gutters were unable to cope with this constant deluge; with water cascading over the side of the roof and streaming down its walls. The old blue wooden sash windows were also weather beaten; and the paint was mostly flaked and cracked, exposing the bare wood to the elements. The garden outside was overgrown and had been "left to the fairies"; so to speak. I surmised that the inhabitants of this quaint old building were probably elderly people; unable to keep on top of routine repairs, and I felt a surge of sympathy for them, hoping they were warm and dry in their atmospheric old home.

As we continued on our way, the path became increasingly waterlogged, muddy, and difficult to negotiate. Small rivulets of water snaked their way down towards us as we struggled against the elements. At times we felt as if we were squelching through a river rather than a footpath.

Consequently, the rainfall had awoken all the small, slimy woodland creatures; and they suddenly appeared in large numbers below our feet.

"Watch out!" I warned the girls. "There are snails, slugs, and... oh look... there's lots of wee tree frogs jumping across the path!" The tiny frogs looked just like insects from above. I stooped down to pick one up and marveled at the minute detail of its delicate legs and pinhead eyes: it was no bigger than my thumbnail. After showing my prize to the girls, I then placed the miniscule creature gently on a blade of grass; which must have seemed as big as a palm tree to the tiny thing.

"Frogs are very cleansing," remarked Lucy. "You must be seeing them for a reason because Clara and I haven't spotted one yet."

That was true, I thought: but couldn't it just be because I've got better eyesight; being the youngest of the three? I kept my opinions to myself, however, and trudged on ahead, continuing to pre-warn the girls of anymore creatures; in case they unwittingly squashed them underfoot.

Just before we got to the wooden sign-post signaling the start of "The Fairy Trail", Lucy began belching again:

"The ghost of Robert Kirk is walking behind you just now Lucy and he is reading a book; I think it's The Bible, but I can't be sure," Clara informed us all, before suddenly changing the subject: *"I can see our auras just now: yours is green Adrian, Lucy's is gold, and mine is purple."*

"What a lovely combination: I wonder why we each have different colours?" I enquired.

"Maybe that's something we'll find out in the future," Lucy replied, and on we trudged. Once in the woodland at the bottom of "Fairy Hill", the walk quickly deteriorated into an arduous slog. Water cascaded down towards us; and the path was a sludgy quagmire.

"At least we should have the place to ourselves today," I said;

trying to remain positive. I turned to look at the girls but neither of them seemed to share in my optimism today. How we managed to get up to "Fairy Tree", I'll never know, but we did, eventually arriving on a wing and a prayer.

Things, however, seemed just as waterlogged at the summit of "Fairy Hill" as on the slopes below. We were all feeling a bit damp and miserable by now and there wasn't a dry spot of ground to sit on, anywhere. There was one consolation though, we did have the place to ourselves and had free reign to be as "away with the fairies" as we wished. We squelched around the trees; reading the sincere messages that were pinned to their trunks, quietly praying that the fairies would answer these wishes. Learning a hard lesson from my last miserly offering; this time I stuck a *pound coin* into the bark of "Fairy Tree" and wished for health and happiness for everyone. Lucy then brought out a small container of bird seed and began ceremoniously sewing the stuff around "Fairy Tree"- that was when the hilarity began:

"There's a dark haired slender male figure, dressed in green clothing, following you around "Fairy Tree"; mimicking your seed-spreading antics Lucy. He's saluting you now that you're finished,"

chuckled Clara.

Picturing the scene, I let out an empathetic laugh but Lucy didn't seem very impressed at the idea of an invisible elf making fun out of one of her rituals; and the expression on her face made me laugh even louder. Then, in a flash of inspiration, Lucy burled round quickly and clicked her camera at the supposed "empty space" where Clara said the figure in green was standing.

"He "cloaked" himself when you did that Lucy, then just shrank into a tiny ball and disappeared," Clara explained.

Lucy and I both stood there speechless! This seemed to spur Clara on further... *"See the foliage behind "Fairy Tree": I don't know if it's me but it looks like a "trapdoor": I can see it rising and falling like a stage."*

With that, the visibly animated Lucy wandered over to the area aforementioned, stood in front of the foliage, and began gyrating up and down in what appeared to be some kind of ritual.

"The "joker" in green was behind you again Lucy: He was imitating your dance. I don't think he means to be cheeky; I think he's just inquisitive; like a curious child. He is such a handsome figure with lovely slender fingers, long dark hair, and thin but well

chiseled features," painted Clara.

I was intrigued myself and couldn't help but venture further into the green "trapdoor" foliage that Clara could see. To me; it appeared like ordinary twisted and jaggy weeds, but it did feel spongy underfoot, and I was secretly praying that the ground below me wouldn't suddenly give way; sending me tumbling into fairyland, where I would be destined to make polite conversation with a 17th century cleric and his olive green buddies for the rest of eternity.

As I was gingerly retracing my steps, the dampness from the persistent rain seemed to be forming a "column of mist" which was swirling, and cascading around me; or was it just mist? At the exact moment I saw the "mist", Clara shouted out in an almost fearful tone:

"They're all around you just now. I just saw all these faces suddenly appear out of the bushes and converge around you."

This time, I was genuinely alarmed, and was so relieved when I returned safely to the girls sporting nothing more than a few bramble scratches. After recovering my composure somewhat, I reached into my bag for a drink of juice, and the girls joined me for some refreshments. As we were all standing together, discussing these exciting events, Clara spotted something out of the corner of her eye:

"I just glimpsed a cream and gold chariot pulled by a white horse, with one solitary male rider; similar to what you would see in the film "Ben Hur"."

"Where?" Lucy and I asked, excitedly.

"It was just a fleeting glance through a gap in the tre... wait a minute... the rider is now standing right in front of me... I... I think it's "The Elf King"! He's got an intricately fashioned crown on his head... it's all scroll work... and his long dark hair is flowing down his shoulders. He's clad in a creamy white cloak, with a fur collar, and he's telling me he's pleased to meet me; and I'm returning the compliment. His horse is just like our horses except finer and more slender in appearance. Ooh, that's him away now- as quick as you like."

Lucy and I just stood there, looking at each other with our faces beaming: Clara had described "The Elf King" pretty much how Robert Kirk had described him in his writings. Clara swore that she'd never so much as heard of Robert Kirk and his exploits before meeting Lucy; and yet she was describing one of the characters from Robert's writings in very accurate detail: It certainly gave credence to Robert's claims. However, the biggest compliment had to be the fact that "The Elf King" and "The Elf Queen" had actually bothered to make an appearance for us at all. What an endorsement for the book, if ever there was one-wouldn't you agree?

One thing we'd forgotten in all this excitement, however, was our intended strawberry offering to the "wee thin five year olds", who by now must have been starving. The "fairy plate" was lying next to "Fairy Tree", having gathered a week's worth of soil and leaves, which Lucy ceremoniously wiped off before placing our offerings on it.

Without warning, Clara grabbed one of the precious strawberries from the container, dropping it onto the mossy ground before the meticulous Lucy had a chance to perform one of her rituals.

"What did you do that for?" Lucy asked inquisitively.

"Oh," blushed Clara, *"One of the "wee thin five year olds" was getting impatient and couldn't wait. He came forward with his hand*

held out so I dropped a strawberry onto his palm. It was really strange to see: a transparent version of the strawberry fell onto his hand and the other part; the bit that everyone sees, fell straight through his hand and onto the ground below. Oh, by the way, I think that these "wee thin five year olds" must be elf children. They look so thin and undernourished, poor wee things," Clara sighed. She then went on to explain to us that the other elf children had waited their turn and shared the strawberries in an adult fashion.

However, even feeding the elf kids seemed like an anti-climax compared to the earlier, majestic appearance of the handsome "Elf King" with his trusty white steed; but we realised that they were just as important.

After the elf kids had eaten, we left, courteously waving as we went.

On our way back down "Fairy Hill", heading towards Aberfoyle, Clara had a spontaneous vision of the Reverend Robert Kirk with tears in his eyes, crying:

"NOW I WILL FINALLY BE BELIEVED!"

CH4 Is it a frog? Is it a chimp? No... It's a goblin! 26.08.09

I awoke this morning full of anticipation and excitement. My strawberry offering was in the fridge; washed and sugared the night before, ready for my trip. Breakfast was a hurried affair, and I hardly took time to even chew my spoonfuls of cornflakes; shoveling them into my mouth: my mind was otherwise focused on limitless possibilities; with the realisation that life was much more exciting than they told us at school: There were other realities out there; a myriad of amazing beings that we could interact with and befriend- if only we had the gift to see them.

Yes, I had read hundreds of books over the years; from the sublime to the ridiculous, but this was one step closer than that: I was now having the adventure of my life with the Reverend Robert Kirk and a load of fairies!

Switching on my mobile phone, I waited in anticipation for a call from the girls, praying that there would be no hiccups to spoil our intended trip back to fairyland. A text came through from Lucy and I eagerly read it, only to be instantly deflated: She wasn't going to make it; one of her relatives wasn't very well. My prayers weren't being answered the way I had hoped but I said a wee prayer for Lucy all the same, and replied with an understanding text in which I tried desperately to mask my disappointment.

So there was one card left to play, so to speak, and that was Clara: With hands shaking in anticipation I phoned her: "Are you still okay for today Clara?"

"Well, I've got important college work to do but I suppose I can manage a couple of hours max," she bargained. *"By the way, is Lucy coming?"*

The question I was dreading. "Lucy can't make it, something's happened," I replied.

"What is it? I hope it isn't anything bad? Is she okay?" enquired a worried Clara.

I had to come out with the truth: "Lucy won't make it today," I explained. "One of her relatives is unwell."

"Well, as a token of respect I think we should give today's trip a miss then too; don't you?" suggested Clara. *"Besides, I've got important college work and I'm behind as it is."*

"Look Clara!" I pleaded. "This is the most important thing that's ever happened to me in my life; in our lives for that matter, and there's no room for sentiment here. You've been gifted with the most amazing "second-sight", and we've been blessed by a visit from none other than "The Elf King" and "Elf Queen". They are obviously keen to make contact with the human kingdom… maybe it's because humanity is senselessly trashing our environment; and subsequently theirs as well- who knows? You have to realise how important this is. Let's just go… PLEASE!" I pleaded.

The phone went dead and I sat alone with my strawberries, silently praying that Clara would turn up. After what seemed like an eternity I heard the sound of a diesel engine drawing up and, instantly recognizing it as Clara's car, I punched the air with relief, rushing out to meet her.

However, I was met with stony silence as I jumped into the passenger seat of her car; as I had half-expected. Clara drove slowly back through the gorgeous rolling hills and greenery of Stirlingshire without so much as a word. In forced silence, I sat admiring the scenery, secretly grateful that I'd eventually got my own way (I know that sounds self-centred but the importance of this experience meant so much to me at the time).

When we arrived in Aberfoyle, the heavens had opened up and we were forced to sit together in the car and brave out the storm. It was strange without the cheery Lucy here; we both missed her bubbly nature and quirky wee rituals.

"Fancy a sandwich Clara?" I asked, trying to break the stony silence.

Half-heartedly, Clara accepted my peace offering:

"Sharing a soggy homemade sandwich with you in my car while it pours outside: I could think of a hundred other things I would rather be doing just now."

"Thanks very much!" I replied; slightly hurt, but it was such a relief to see her warming a wee bit more towards me. We were both hungry and made short work of the sandwiches. I then began to eye up the fairies' strawberries. Clara spotted me:

"Come on now, these are for the "wee thin fairy kids". I think you've eaten enough," she rightfully pointed out.

"Just a couple," I compromised, popping a handful of the delicious red fruits into my mouth. "Look, there's still plenty for the elf kids," I spluttered, spraying Clara with strawberry juice.

"Thanks for the shower," moaned Clara, mopping her face with

a tissue. "Let's go while there's still some strawberries left!"

With that, she jumped out of the dry comfortable car and into the teeming rain. I eagerly followed, full of adventure, despite the gloomy weather. Squelching behind Clara as she forged ahead, it was arguably wetter than our previous visits and, although we were both protected by waterproofs, it was still an arduous trek. Clara made it quite plain that I still wasn't "flavour of the month", however, and I really had to increase my pace to catch up with her.

We eventually arrived at the cemetery gates and decided to pay our respects to Robert Kirk, more as a gesture to the absent Lucy as we felt that this is what she would have done if she'd been here with us today. Suddenly, Clara heard a disembodied voice saying: *"Where is the fair one today?"*

"I take it they, whoever they are, are referring to Lucy," I suggested; stating the obvious in an attempt to start some congenial dialogue with Clara. However, Clara just nodded curtly in reply. Before we entered the cemetery though Clara was suddenly arrested by a ghostly vision:

"I just saw an old-fashioned horse-drawn hearse go past just now," she exclaimed. *"The hearse was empty and was being pulled*

by two dark horses wearing black plumes," she added.

Unfortunately, that's all I was getting today; running commentaries and nothing more. Once inside the cemetery gates we stared around at the place: It seemed as barren as before; devoid of any colour, save for a handful of artificial wreaths that lay dotted around here and there. There wasn't a soul in sight as we made our way over to Robert Kirk's Grave: It stood there, chipped, weather-beaten and bare; a forgotten relic in a wilderness of old forgotten relics. A sudden warmth filled my heart though as I recalled the nature of the man through his wonderful writings.

"This place is as bleak as ever," I moaned.

Trying my best to ignore the uncomfortable feeling of "soggy sock syndrome", I joined Clara for the rest of our journey back up to "Fairy Tree". We trudged on and, despite the persistent heavy rain, I noticed there wasn't a tree frog in sight. All I could see was the occasional light brown slug dotted here and there. Even the tree frogs weren't daft enough to venture out on a day like this- we must have been mad! However, as we were walking up the path towards "The Fairy Trail" there were others, invisible to my naked eye, who were obviously unaffected by the driving wind and rain...

"Several tiny creatures just rushed past us," Clara gasped. *"They were travelling so fast I could barely count them. I think there were five- maybe more."*

My next question was a bit silly, in hindsight, but I asked it all the same: "What did they look like?"

"I couldn't see: they were a blur as they rushed past. All I can say is they were less than a metre tall," answered Clara.

Once we'd arrived in the woodland at the start of "The Fairy Trail", Clara was sure she could see the small "Roadrunner-type" creatures that had whizzed past us a few minutes before:

"Oh, look up in the trees; it's them I think. They're hanging from the branches like little monkeys, peering down at us," she gasped.

I think Clara temporarily forgot, in her excitement, that my eyes were still firmly tuned to the human world because, when I looked up, all I could see were trees, trees, and more trees! Once we were in the surrounding woodland, however, Clara's "second-sight" began to accelerate further and she started giving me a running commentary on all the magical and wonderful things she could see:

"There are lots of wee "fairy animals" grazing just now; they look like miniature deer and, as we're approaching them, they're going to ground; motionless. I feel they can sense that I can see them. Oh, I wish you could see how vibrant this place is today!" she exclaimed, as the intensity of her "second-sight" began to take hold...

"The pebbles are glowing, sparkling; radiating their life force," Clara added excitedly. *"I can hear voices now,"* she informed me. *"They're saying: "Oh you're a goddess are you?" I think they are jokingly referring to my handbag."* (Sure enough, Clara's handbag had the word "goddess" printed on its side in large red lettering.)

I laughed at their joke and Clara replied aloud: *"I'm not a goddess; I'm just a humble human."*

"They just said to me: "Not so humble- Not so humble" when I said that," continued Clara with her running commentary.

Because of the horrendous weather conditions it was a hard slog up to "Fairy Tree", battling the liquefied mud and gravel beneath our feet. We were so relieved when we eventually reached the summit. However, once we'd arrived we were greeted by a sodden mess- and the trees offered little protection from the downpour. There wasn't a dry spot to sit on anywhere.

We both stood together for a while; like a couple of haddock in a fishmonger's window, staring at the dripping foliage in front of us. This didn't dampen Clara's spirits though and she tied a flag to "Fairy Tree"; asking for peace, harmony, and love for the world. While she was doing this I removed the lid from the container of strawberries, gently placing them at the bottom of "Fairy Tree".

"Aw, the "wee thin elf kids" are having a dance together before going to the strawberries- they are so cute!" described Clara, before correcting me again:

"You shouldn't have done that. You should have taken the strawberries from the container and put them on the "fairy plate". They're crowded round the container; all of them trying to get in at the same time... wait a minute... they're all gone now," she continued.

"Have they eaten them already? Goodness me, that was quick!" I asked, and answered myself at the same time.

"No, they grabbed a couple each and went off into the woods with them," replied Clara instantly.

"Just out of curiosity Clara, how do these creatures appear to you?" I enquired.

"It's just like flashes I'm seeing at times; not the full picture- it's hard to describe," she explained politely.

"You described it exactly as I've read in some books Clara," I reassured her. "Some people I've read about, who claim to be "sensitive", describe this other, invisible world around them as appearing to them in "flashes"," I explained.

"That's comforting to know," replied Clara with a reassured smile. *"It's just, sometimes, I can't help thinking that I'm maybe a wee bit crazy when no-one else sees what I see."*

"That's understandable Clara; you're bound to feel that way at times but I can assure you that most of what you describe seeing I've read about before in books, and even I doubted it until I met you." I gave her a comforting smile which was returned with a look of ABSOLUTE TERROR as Clara stared, goggle-eyed, over my shoulder. I turned around in an instant, only to be confronted by a bank of "swirling mist". Her eyes transfixed with fear and, in between short sharp breaths of sheer panic, Clara began stuttering:

"Th... they... they're all around us nnnow... all around us... all ssshapes and sizes; staring at us intently!" The expression on Clara's face was disconcerting, to say the least, and I was a wee bit concerned about what "this invisible horde" would do next. I had no sooner thought this when the "mist" began to recede in front of my eyes. At that exact moment Clara let out a sigh of pure relief:

"They're all leaving now- THANK GOODNESS!" We both slumped back against "Fairy Tree", exhausted by our encounter. I quickly grabbed a bottle of orange juice and we both moistened our dry throats. Clara slowly began to recover her composure; her speech and breathing returned to a normal, rhythmical flow:

"I... I don't think these beings intended to frighten us; they were just curious," Clara reassured me (I think the fairies must have sensed our fear because we were standing for a good fifteen minutes after our encounter and Clara was seeing nothing.) It really was damp and miserable by now and I could feel the moisture in the air permeate through my clothes. It felt like it was penetrating my skin, right into my bones, and I shuddered involuntarily: "Let's go Clara. I think we've both seen enough for

one day."

Clara shivered in sympathy, but, just as we were about to negotiate the treacherous descent back down "Fairy Hill", she suddenly halted in her tracks; arrested by another vision:

""The Elf King" has just appeared between the trees in front of me. He's standing next to his white horse; giving me a reassuring smile," Clara described, with a transfixed stare.

Responding to Clara's reaction of fascination, I probed further: "Describe the scene please Clara," I urged.

"Oh, he's mesmerizing to look at: finely chiseled features with long black hair framing his handsome face. He's wearing a wonderful cream cloak with a fine collar that looks as if it's made from the softest of fur. The reason I'm sure he's "The Elf King" is because he's wearing a crown on his head... now he's gone; as quick as that!"

"Now a very lovely woman has just appeared in front of me; she looks like "The Elf Queen" but says she isn't, and is only a member of "The Queen's Council". She's dressed in a long cream gown. I can't even see her feet; her gown is so long. Over her gown she's wearing a green overcoat."

So there she was, a beautiful member of "The Queen's Council", addressing the humble Clara:

"She's reassuring us about the horde of fairy folk I saw earlier; telling me not to be afraid. They were just curious and wanted to see the "seer"- if you catch my drift?" continued a calmer Clara.

"Can I ask her a couple of questions?" I begged.

"She says that you're more than welcome," Clara confirmed.

"Okay then, what is your name madam?" I asked politely.

"She says her name is "Aarkeesha", or something like that: It's very long and difficult to pronounce," replied Clara on behalf of the lady elf (Robert Kirk mentions in his writings that the elves had very long names that were difficult to pronounce, and he would shorten them to "nicknames" so he could remember them. Clara was unaware of this at the time.)

"That's a lovely name. How old are you Aarkeesha?" I enquired.

"She's refusing to give you her age," Clara replied.

"That's okay: I shouldn't ask a lady her age anyway; it's rude. Thank you for your time Aarkeesha. It was good of you to speak with me," I finished humbly.

Clara informed me that the "Queen's helper" had to go but she would try to speak to us again later (Unfortunately, that didn't happen).

"She's thanking you for the strawberries you gave her children and says you have a kind heart," said Clara, smiling.

I began to blush at the compliment and replied that I felt honoured by her kind words. With that, I bade her farewell (Call it my imagination, but I swear I could feel the affection from this elf lady radiating from where Clara told me she was standing). By this time, Clara and I were now drenched to the skin, but the trip had been well worth it!

We negotiated our descent back down "Fairy Hill" with the utmost of care as the path was muddy and waterlogged underfoot. The heavy rain had liquefied the stony ground beneath our feet, making the pebbles loose and treacherous to stand on.

We both breathed a deep sigh of relief when we eventually reached the bottom of the slope, and we stood for a moment peering back through that enchanting, green-carpeted woodland:

"I can see "The Elf King" again. He's riding the white horse bareback at tremendous speed, hugging the beast like a jockey, his head tight to the horse's neck. He's clad in the same cream cloak,

and his long dark hair is cascading down his back," painted Clara.

What a description! Even I could picture this handsome "Elf King" riding "hell for leather" through the woodland on his trusty steed; like something out of "Wuthering Heights". Well, that alone would have been a glorious end to a day of mixed blessings; but there was more to follow...

In the thick of the woods stands a moss covered rock. There's nothing special about this rock. Clara, Lucy, and I have walked past this spot several times before without so much as a second glance- but today would be different:

"There's a creature; a VERY UGLY CREATURE sitting squat on top of that rock just now. Yuck, it looks like a giant frog!" Clara squirmed.

I stood, my eyes transfixed on the rock, perhaps fortunate enough to see nothing: "Would it be too much if I asked you to describe the creature in more detail?" I enquired, hopefully.

"Yes it would!" replied Clara sharply. "Okay then, I'll try: It is brown/green in colour, with sharp beady eyes and pointed ears- and it's got oily wet skin... yuck... that's all you're getting!"

Ignoring Clara's pleas not to go back; I returned to the rock, armed with my camera phone and took a quick couple of photos of the area where Clara said the creature was sitting and- you guessed it- I got absolutely nothing but a rock when I reviewed my pictures. Disappointed, I made my way back towards a visibly shaken Clara; and you would have thought I had just turned into a "Werewolf" by the look she was giving me...

"That creature has just jumped down from its "granite perch" and is following you right now!" She shrieked.

I felt the hairs standing up on the back of my neck. I'd read in books, and seen programs on T.V. about people being followed home by unwanted, invisible entities that they'd met in desolate areas, and I didn't fancy the prospect of sharing my flat with an invisible, but very ugly, giant frog-like creature, so I turned round nervously and addressed the "empty space" where Clara said the creature was standing: "Goodbye, I'll see you later... or should I say... I won't see you later... In fact, I'll hopefully never... ever... set eyes on you for the rest of my life!"

Clara seemed calmer now and more at ease as she described what happened next:

"The creature seems to have a sense of humour, because, after

you'd spoken, it giggled with its shoulders, then turned around and bounded back towards its rock; moving much like a chimpanzee would." There's maybe a lesson to be learnt here: We should "never judge a book by its cover"!

We both ambled back to Clara's car, visibly relieved that we weren't being followed by a "giant frog" that runs like a chimpanzee. That encounter was to be the first of many with a very special goblin!

CH5 Grozwald isn't ugly; he's windswept and fun 06.09.09

Lucy was back; we were together again in full force, and were officially "The Treeheads" again. Her relative was recovering well, and Lucy was keen to re-establish her links with The Reverend Robert Kirk and his stomping ground; the wonderful Aberfoyle. So we arrived once more in this picturesque part of Scotland, full of adventure and anticipation.

"It's my turn to buy the strawberries today," insisted an animated Lucy. "I'm just going to visit the ladies room, then popping over to the shops. Will you both wait for me in the car?"

So Clara and I waited, and waited, but there was still no sign of Lucy.

"Where has she got to?" wondered Clara; echoing my sentiments exactly.

"I don't know, but we've sat here for long enough. Let's go into the village and see if we can find her," I suggested. We checked out all the shops, the public toilet and visitor centre, but she was nowhere to be seen.

"Let's just head up towards "Fairy Hill"; maybe we missed her and she's gone on ahead," I guessed. As we were walking towards the cemetery, I was sure I could see Lucy in the distance; recognizing her by her cut off trousers and shoes, but she was much too far away to shout after. As we were on a very tight schedule that day, and it was already mid-afternoon, we made our apologies to Robert as we rushed past the cemetery on our way up to "Fairy Hill". However, to get to the summit of "Fairy Hill", we would have to pass the rock where Clara had previously spied the ugly "frog-like" creature, and neither Clara nor I relished the prospect; but morbid curiosity got the better of us both. We sheepishly approached the impending rock with Clara gingerly standing several metres behind me. Out of the blue, suddenly, Clara shouted out:

"IT'S THERE, IT'S THERE! I can see it sitting squat on top of the rock. Please be careful."

I gingerly approached the rock while Clara stood at a safe distance, giving me a running commentary on the creature's antics:

"It's just jumped off its rock and is running around you just now saying: "ME- ME- ME- Write about ME!"" (Well there you have it; its

wish has been granted).

Clara then began to move closer, once the creature had started to speak; visibly calmer, knowing it could communicate with us. So I decided to attempt speaking with the creature, feeling that I'd established some kind of rapport with it:

"What's your name and what are you?" I asked it; directing my question to what looked just like an empty space: It was obviously keen to be on centre stage because it shared much more information with me than I had initially asked it for; albeit through Clara, in "Pidgin English":

"Me Grozwald- Me over a hundred years old- I have wife too- She much prettier than your wife- She called Gorlinda."

Roaring with laughter; I put my arm around a rather bemused Clara:

"This isn't my wife Grozwald; this is my good friend Clara, and what you said wasn't very nice." But Grozwald didn't seem to understand what nice meant and seemed to speak very directly, and without diplomacy, according to what Clara was picking up.

"It doesn't speak very good English, does it?" I observed, directing my questioning towards Clara: "Where did it learn?"

Clara then went on to explain that Grozwald was informing us both that he was a creature known as a "goblin", and that they learned their English over the years by listening to the locals speaking: She told me that as long as there was woodland nearby, the goblins could venture in as close as they liked, and listen to the language being spoken (Let's face it, after more than 100 years of living in Aberfoyle; you're bound to pick up a few words, aren't you?- Hopefully more than Grozwald, anyway.)

So there he stood, no longer an ugly creature with no name but now a fine goblin with a name that sounded as if it came from "The Hobbit", and speaking as much English as you'd find on the back of a soup can label. But hey, this was Grozwald and who would change him for anything?

We said our goodbyes, but before we left, Grozwald warned Clara to beware of "The Creatures of the Dark" who weren't kind to humans. It was now late afternoon and the light was beginning to fade, so Grozwald's warning made us feel a bit wary as we entered the shaded woodland at the bottom of the hill.

"This Grozwald character seems to have taken quite a shine to you Adrian; he's right behind you just now, and seems to be

following you," smiled Clara.

Not keen on the thought of being followed by anyone, especially a "giant frog" that runs like a chimpanzee, I turned round to face him and politely said my goodbyes. He must have got the message because Clara could no longer see him behind us anymore as we continued our trek up the winding path to "Fairy Tree". When we eventually reached the summit we were met by Lucy who was sitting on a dry moss-covered log, holding a sprig of green fir cones in her right hand:

"I found this branch lying next to the tree: Look; it's still got pine cones attached and makes a great noise when you shake it," announced an excited Lucy. She proceeded to give us all a demonstration: It sounded much like a child's rattle, I thought.

"Looks like a fairy with wings doesn't it?" Lucy remarked excitedly. "I'm going to do a "healing" on you both with this," she insisted.

"Why don't I go first? Clara can watch and write down what she sees," I suggested eagerly.

Both girls agreed, so I stood near the "trap-door" area that Clara had described on our previous visit, while Lucy began working on me. As she was doing her magic, or whatever alternative healers do, it began to rain; and as the rain drops filtered through the trees they fell on my face like a cool mist, refreshing my body and soul. Lucy spent a good fifteen to twenty minutes with me and, as she was working, I could hear Clara's frantic scribbling in the background, and I was so desperate to see what she had written down.

I had had healing sessions from Lucy in the past, and they were very powerful experiences, but I had never had a gifted "seer" with me at the same time. The session ended, and I felt invigorated and refreshed.

After a very brief but genuine thank you, I darted over to Clara like a youngster on Christmas Day:

"What did you see?" I begged.

Clara showed me her rough sketch. I'll describe her visions in her own words:

"I could see a green aura around you both when Lucy was working on you. There was a V-shaped vortex above your head Adrian and the longer Lucy worked on you; the wider the vortex became. Lucy wasn't working alone though; there was a mysterious

figure with her all the time: This figure had long white hair, and was wearing a cloak of feathers. In his right hand he carried a stick which had two feathers sticking out of the top of the shaft (Sounds like the Aztec God "Quetzecoatl", doesn't it? Incidentally, the wearing of feathers is supposed to increase sensitivity. I don't need to remind anyone that the American Indian Tribes were known for wearing feathers and they are well known for their sensitivity).

So it was Clara's turn to get her healing next- and you guessed right again- I didn't see a thing!

After a ceremonious thank you by Lucy and Clara to the invisible helpers around us, we gingerly made our way back down "Fairy Hill" to Clara's car.

Clara didn't see any elves today. Maybe they were all having a big banquet somewhere deep underground in "The Elf Caverns".

Also, Grozwald's "Creatures of the Dark" failed to show up. Were they saving themselves for a later chapter I wonder?

CH6 Grozwald's babies 08.09.09

If you've found this book difficult to believe so far, I would like to take the opportunity of pre-warning you that the chapter you're about to read even I had difficulty believing; but I trust Clara implicitly. She is a quiet, humble person who seeks neither fame nor notoriety. So here are her encounters; written down as they happened, and I can assure you that none of the dialogue she had from any of the beings in Aberfoyle that day was altered in any way, nor anytime in the whole book for that matter. Now back to the story...

I was in a nice peaceful dream-sleep when my phone rudely jolted me back to reality:

"Guess what? I've got an interview for a job in Aberfoyle. I'm so excited!" blurted out an ecstatic Clara.

"Don't get too excited, you haven't been offered the job yet," I replied.

"Trust you, the eternal pessimist," Clara retorted.

"I'm not a pessimist," I replied defensively, "I'm a realist, and I'm sure you'll do well at the interview but you haven't got the job yet. We'll celebrate when you have."

Being a realist; but at the same time a firm believer in fairies (Yes, it is possible), I jumped at the chance of a free trip to Aberfoyle:

"I hope you don't mind me asking Clara but would it be okay to hitch a ride with you? I could get some strawberries and we could visit the elf folk on our way back."

"If you think I'm trudging up "Fairy Hill" in my smart interview suit and shiny shoes then you've got another thing coming!" replied Clara sternly.

"Okay then, what if you accompany me up to "Grozwald's Rock" and I'll run up "Fairy Hill" as quick as I can and drop off the strawberries. I'll be back quicker than you can say "Hansel and Gretel"-I promise!"

"You drive a hard bargain," Clara sighed. *"Okay, but I'm not staying long!*

Oh and by the way, what about Lucy? Maybe she wants to come along as well?" suggested a thoughtful Clara.

"She can't; she's visiting her boyfriend just now," I reminded her.

"Oh yes of course... silly me... I was so focused on my interview

that I totally forgot," replied Clara.

So we headed off in the car together towards Aberfoyle. It was a very warm day and Clara was all fingers and thumbs with her nerves and, believe it or not, we got LOST! We drove around the Aberfoyle area for what seemed like ages, doubling back on ourselves numerous times, but we just couldn't find the place. Being a "fire sign"(Sagittarius), I was beginning to get rather hot under the collar:

"Why didn't you take down the phone number of the place and you could have called them?" I grumbled.

But Clara maintained her cool, like the good "water sign" (Pisces) she is, and gave me an apologetic smile. Eventually, we finally arrived at our destination with seconds to spare; Clara rushing into a large modern building for her interview. I felt sorry for her as she must've been exhausted with the journey-I know I was and collapsed into the backseat of her car, flat out, with my legs tightly pressed up against the side window. I must've dozed off because, the next thing I knew, Clara was standing outside peering at me through the car window, her face beaming:

"I've got the job; they want me to start as soon as possible!" she

squealed in delight. *"The coffees are on me," insisted an ecstatic Clara. "Let's head into the village and visit our favourite cafe."*

"Remember our intended visit to "Fairy Hill"," I reminded her (I think she was hoping I wouldn't mention it). Clara reluctantly acknowledged my request before we headed into the cafe. We sat with our coffees for longer than I had hoped and, when we did eventually leave, the light was fading fast and there was now a distinct chill in the air. As Clara half-hobbled up the rough path towards "Fairy Wood" in her best shoes, I suddenly felt a twinge of guilt for dragging her up here. By the time we reached "Grozwald's Rock" it was cold, and everything was in semi-darkness. Clara then stopped in front of "The Rock" with her arms crossed, desperately trying to keep warm. Once she'd regained her composure, however, she peered into the dark undergrowth:

"I can see Grozwald and what looks like a female goblin: They're both standing on top of their rocky outcrop"... She then peered even closer:

"Aw... They must have three children as well. I can see them standing by their parents. They look like "cupid dolls"; with pointed ears and fat bellies"... She continued describing them:

"They've got a tiny tuft of hair on their heads and they're about the size of newborn babies. Their arms and legs are spindly, and they've got a lime-green sheen to their skin... Oh, and they're all naked!"

I stood laughing incredulously at her descriptions of Grozwald's babies but I trusted Clara's abilities, and her total honesty. She continued describing the baby goblins:

"I think they're triplets; all girls. They look like their mother, and they're hanging on to her... Oh, one of them just came forward and drooled a salivary smile... They are so cute!" she cooed.

I listened in amazement, but at the same time the night was drawing in and I didn't want to hang about for too long. Before I left to climb "Fairy Hill", however, I held out a strawberry in the area Clara said the goblin family were standing in:

"Grozwald just stuck out his tongue and said "YUCK!"" Clara informed me.

"I take it that's a NO then? Could you ask him what they DO like to eat; so I know what to bring him in the future?" I enquired thoughtfully.

"Oh... He says he just likes to forage for berries and plants in the

local area," Clara replied.

"That suits me fine and saves me a few pennies," I replied; as I held on to my tight Scots wallet. With a half-hearted goodbye wave in the direction of what seemed to me like an "empty space", I turned towards Clara:

"It's okay, I won't be long", I reassured her, before grabbing the strawberries and rushing deeper into the woodland:

I was surprised at how dark it was; deep inside the wood, as I puffed and panted up the hill towards "Fairy Tree". This place had a deathly silence about it tonight, save for the occasional rustle in the undergrowth as startled woodland creatures scurried away at the sound of my heavy footsteps and panting breath. This, in turn, startled me; so I suppose they got their revenge, didn't they?

Eventually, I arrived at the foot of "Fairy Tree", exhausted. By this time it was pitch black and my thoughts turned to Clara; standing on her own in a desolate spot, in the cold and darkness. I then remembered Grozwald's previous mention of "The Creatures of the Dark" who supposedly came out at night. I began to get extremely nervous at the thought and hurriedly dumped the strawberries on the "fairy plate" which was lying below "Fairy

Tree". They spilled unceremoniously onto the ground so I apologized to "the invisible horde" I was sure must've been gathering round me just now, then, turning around quickly, I sped back down the hill as fast as I could. Call me a coward and cover me in custard but, to be honest, I couldn't get down "Fairy Hill" quickly enough, and was so relieved to find Clara safe and well, her silhouette standing against "The Rock" as I'd left her.

Clara seemed equally pleased to see me and gave me a relieved smile:

"It was beginning to get a wee bit chilly here- and spooky as well," she shivered.

"Sorry Clara, I didn't mean to keep you so long. It was selfish of me and I regretted it the instant I left you," I panted; out of breath.

"What an experience I've had here while you were away!" she blurted out.

"Like what?" I asked excitedly.

"Well... Apparently Grozwald has a neighbour who lives in the bush over there and he calls himself "Grazzby"," replied an animated Clara. *"This Grazzby character told me he doesn't like Grozwald: I somehow get the impression he's jealous because*

Grozwald has a pretty wife and he hasn't. I think he's an eligible bachelor; desperate for a partner. I didn't want to continue talking to this "Grazzby" character because jealously is never a nice trait in any being, so I politely turned my back on him"... and then she briefly paused, as if waiting for encouragement.

"It's okay; continue... you know how open-minded I am. What else did you get?" I enquired eagerly.

"Well... I asked Grozwald the names of his 3 children and burst out laughing when he told me- much to his annoyance. I really thought the goblins were joking at first, but apparently not."

"Okay... Okay... Don't keep me in suspense," I said, with the grin widening on my face: "SHARE IT!"

Clara paused and took a deep breath before emerging with the punch line:

"Okay then... Wait for it... His kids' names are...... "SIPPIT", "LIPPIT", and "DIPPIT" (Clara had also found this exceptionally amusing because "DIPPIT" is also a Scots word which means "daft" or "stupid". I don't think the goblin family were aware of this and we didn't think it would be helpful to inform them.)

Well, I shrieked with laughter and probably woke up every

goblin in the woods!

"Shoosh!" Clara scolded. *"Don't add insult to injury. I think I've offended them enough, don't you?"*

I quickly placed a hand over my mouth to stifle my mirth and, when I'd regained my composure, I turned to face Clara, still chuckling silently:

"Surely you are joking! Why did they pick names like that?" I giggled. But, I could see by the solemn expression on Clara's face that she wasn't joking.

Waiting for my laughter to die down first, Clara then began to explain:

"Grozwald told me he gave his kids their names because of the way they eat their food: One sips her food, the other lips at hers, and the last one dips." (Maybe the goblins were playing games with us, who knows? Goblins are apparently known, in folklore, to be mischievous at times).

Well, I turned my back to "The Rock", held my hand over my mouth, and started belly laughing uncontrollably. Eventually, I came to my senses though, and turned round to face Clara:

"Well, I suppose that's one way of naming your kids...

goodness me... if my parents had followed that line of logic I could've been christened "Soup-Slurper Bain"- and why not?"

Clara smirked at my comment; fuelling my ego further. We waved goodbye to the goblin family and, as we were heading back to the car, I continued to suggest more "Eating-Habits Christian Names":

"What's the name of that top T.V. chef who has his face on just about every cookery book on the planet? If his parents had christened him "Gravy Drool", do you think he would've been as successful as he is today?"

"Obviously not," groaned Clara. *"Anyway, you've taken that joke too far."*

CH7 Fairies say prayers too, you know 12.09.09

Today was the Twelfth of September. To me it was just like any other day, or at least that's what I thought, as Clara drove us both into Falkirk to pick up Lucy. However, as the car drew closer to Lucy's house, I could see her standing there waiting but her body posture instantly told me all was not well. Opening the car door Lucy slumped into the back seat, tears streaming down her face.

Clara was visibly as uncomfortable as I was, and neither of us knew what to do, so we both opted for silence as the best option.

They say that time is a great healer and, after about fifteen minutes of uncontrollable sobbing, Lucy began to utter a few words; in between sniffles:

"It's my... sob... sniff... boyfriend," she wailed; and then went on to describe a disagreement they'd both had over the phone.

Knowing that Lucy saw her boyfriend rarely; due to his work commitments, I tried to imagine how difficult it must have been for her. I reached over and gently squeezed her shoulder. Lucy raised her head briefly, and her tear-glazed eyes seemed to respond to my sympathies.

We all sat in silence for the full journey; the heavy atmosphere from Lucy's grief dictated that.

It was a beautiful autumn day when we arrived in Aberfoyle, and even the love-struck Lucy seemed to brighten in mood the moment she was exposed to the woody autumn smells that so often pervade the air in a small country village like this. I decided to strike while the iron was hot:

"Let's go for some refreshments at the wee tea room- my treat."

Once inside the café, the aroma of fresh baking and roasted coffee were like smelling salts to Lucy; bringing her back to the here and now; reconnecting her with precious moments spent in this enchanting place, and with the realization that we were about to embark on another fascinating adventure with the fairies. Consequently, Lucy seemed to slowly transform back into "The Treehead" she undoubtedly was, and soon Clara and I couldn't get a word in edge ways:

"I wonder what you'll see today Clara? It's amazing; that gift you've got... you know... "second-sight": I'm so excited!"

"Yes, it can be amazing", Clara soberly agreed. "But it can also be extremely harrowing as well. Some of the things I've seen in my life have also been quite upsetting; so it's a "double-edged sword" really."

Lucy became suddenly solemn again in response to Clara's blunt reply, and Clara, recognizing this, squeezed Lucy's hand gently, giving her a reassuring smile. With that, I settled the bill and we stepped out of the tea room, suitably refreshed and ready for another adventure.

Bright autumn days are rare in Scotland, and lots of people were making the most of the fine weather today. Everyone was out and about, cycling, recycling, walking their dogs- you name it. People who would normally be forced to stay indoors had suddenly appeared outside in great numbers. In fact, I was surprised at potentially what a large population Scotland may actually have. Maybe there are many more than 5 million people in Scotland; it's just the weather that keeps them from being counted in the numbers.

As we approached the old quaint cottage that looked as if it had been built during the lifetime of Robert Kirk himself, we spied an elderly lady standing outside, wrestling with an antiquated lawn mower twice her own size, making a brave attempt at what seemed to be an impossible task of trying to tame her wild garden. As we were passing by, I was sorely tempted to stop and ask her a few questions about Robert Kirk and the fairies. I couldn't resist the chance, and asked the kindly lady a few simple questions about the legend but she was unable to help me so I politely thanked her, and took my leave.

Further up the hill, we spotted a younger woman mowing the lawn of a much larger garden in which was set an old house; younger than the cottage but still in my estimations at least a couple of centuries old. Not wanting to pass up a second opportunity of getting some free information about Aberfoyle, Lucy and I entered her garden and approached the woman, who appeared quite congenial at first. She told us that the grand old building behind her was erected in the 18th century, and that the once legendary Walter Scott had stayed there for some time as a guest (Walter Scott was a Scottish writer who was interested in fairy legends and wrote several books on the subject. I don't think I need to explain the reasons for his stay in Aberfoyle*)*. I then explained to the woman that I was writing a book but Lucy gave me a gentle nudge in the ribs; stopping me in my tracks before I gave too much information away. The woman then appeared to become equally guarded, and told us her husband was writing a book about the area as well, but that's all she would divulge- end of conversation.

Well, that was a brief account of our polite but short conversations with our fellow humankind, so now let's get on with the interesting stuff:

As we were approaching "Grozwald's Rock"; a grand old stone structure consisting of one large moss-covered lump of rock, probably erected in pre-historic times, and surrounded by a wild garden (not a lawn mower in sight), Clara let out an exclamation of delight:

"He's there: I can see him standing on top of "The Rock"... Now he's jumped off and is following us up "Fairy Hill"."

I quickly turned around and acknowledged the invisible goblin with a gentle nod of the head. Lucy smiled at how foolish I must've looked: She still wasn't brave enough to address a being she couldn't see, but her respect for Clara's talents were, none the less, very high.

The woods were an absolute joy to walk through today. We were buffeted by a gentle breeze, and the sunlight filtering through the trees created a dappling effect on the surrounding foliage; adding more depth and enchantment to the place.

Now this chapter wouldn't be the same without a burp from Lucy and I bet you were all wondering when it was coming? Well, just before we got to the summit of "Fairy Hill", Lucy let out her characteristic "belly rumble":

"Burrrrrrrppp... That's better!" she said, rubbing her tummy, and then collapsing onto a large mossy log. We both joined her. It's amazing how comfortable a damp old piece of log feels after a long trek uphill, and let's face it, none of us are getting any younger: Clara and I are in our forties with "big sis" Lucy able to count a few more "rings on her trunk". But we "Treeheads" are wearing well. Maybe it's on account of our belief in fairies that keeps us young at heart- who knows?

"Grozwald's standing right behind us just now," Clara enlightened us both.

"Hi Grozwald!" I shouted, as I turned round quickly; holding out a strawberry in friendship.

"Watch out! You nearly poked Grozwald in the belly when you held out that strawberry. He had to retreat back quickly to avoid you," Clara warned me.

"Well, now he knows how "The Invisible Man" must've felt when he got too close to the competitors in a kick-boxing competition," I joked.

"That's him taken the essence of the strawberry; it's now been eaten," Clara added. *"It's strange seeing him up so close at eye level: he's got long spindly fingers and long nails,"* she continued.

"By the way, where is Grozwald's wife today?" asked Lucy, with a half-smile on her face.

"Where she should be!" came back the instantaneous reply from Clara's lips; suggesting goblin females had the old traditional role of wife and mother.

"This place seems deserted today," remarked an intuitive Lucy.

"You're right Lucy; the place is empty," confirmed Clara. *"The elves aren't here today; it's their day of prayer."*

"Oh, so elves believe in God as well. What about you Grozwald; do you believe?" I asked, directing my question towards the empty space Clara assured me he was standing in. Clara answered in Grozwald's distinctive Pidgin tongue:

"Goblins don't say prayers- Goblins lookouts."

"Oh, the equivalent of our security guards," I joked, "long hours and terrible pay." This got a giggle from Lucy, and I was relieved she was still smiling, despite boyfriend troubles.

Clara continued with some more "Grozwaldspeak": *"Only goblins and other creatures around today. Be wary of dark creatures- Negative- Come out at night- You okay- You in circle- Protected."*

Clara then began describing "Fairy Tree": *"It's emitting a different colour today; a golden green with a softer hue to it. It's gently glowing today, rather than sending out rays."*

I sat back in amazement listening to Clara's visions, totally in awe to be honest. As for Lucy, she appeared immersed in deep thought, and seemed to be missing out on a lot of the action today. Clara noticed that Lucy was sitting with her arms crossed:

"That's how Robert Kirk's body was laid out: in the sign of the St. Andrews cross; it's supposed to protect against evil spirits. The Egyptians apparently did the same with their dead."

"The Egyptian/Scottish connection!" I exclaimed. "The word

"Scot" is supposed to originate from Egypt. I remember reading it in a book somewhere." Lucy suddenly interrupted with a shiver:

"Brrrr... I've suddenly come over all cold. Hope I'm not coming down with something."

"No, it's the spirit of Robert Kirk: He's standing very close to you just now," explained Clara. *"Ask him to stand back."*

With innocent courtesy; holding out my container of fruit, I turned towards Lucy and asked: "Does Robert want a strawberry?"

There were hoots of laughter all round before Lucy composed herself enough to say: "He's dead! How can he have a strawberry?"

Feeling a wee bit embarrassed by my own silly comment, I decided to busy myself; gently placing a selection of grapes, raspberries, and strawberries on the "fairy plate", while at the same time asking Clara for a running commentary:

"I can see lots of goblin creatures; all different shapes and sizes. They've all taken handfuls of fruit and left. Grozwald has left too, following close behind them. They must be his friends or something. There were 9 of them- Grozwald makes 10. I can also see lots of faces in the bushes watching us all the time... wait... I can hear

some sort of chanting in the distance: must be the elves in prayer: Sounds like: "Ahlugh... Ahlugh... Ahlugh... Och... Sain... Ach... Ach": Like Gaelic: It's very hard to repeat what they're chanting; their language sounds like singing, the words are running into each other."

"Today is Saturday, but I'm sure that Saturday used to be the original Sabbath," I observed. "In fact, I'm positive the Orthodox Jews still worship on a Saturday to this very day."

"That's funny," interjected Lucy; suddenly changing the subject: "I remember September 12th last year. I was feeling very emotional on that day also... couldn't let go of my friend... wanted to hug her forever."

"I got up and, leaving the girls for a wee while, decided to go for a wander on my own. Passing the trees in "The Circle", I stopped briefly to read some of the wishes tied to their branches: One wish was tied on with shiny blue ribbon and was obviously penned by a love struck teenage girl; wishing the boy she liked would like her back (I hope your wish was granted). I continued walking past Clara's "trap-door" area, and around the periphery of "The Circle". The undergrowth felt like "Velcro" under my feet;

grabbing and tugging constantly at my jeans. I then continued along a small dirt track, leading me into a clearing in the woods; and from this amazing vantage point I had a wonderful view of the woodland and rolling hills below. The air was completely still today and the acoustics of the valley below made every sound audible. I could hear the distant trickle of running water, and the sound of crows cawing in the treetops. As I stood gazing at the breathtaking scenery, the sun was setting on my right, and the lush countryside was bathed in a golden glow. I could see small specks moving down in the valley below me. Screwing up my eyes, I could make out the tiny figures of a group of people out cycling for the day. Feeling suitably refreshed from my wee jaunt, I continued my circular walk and rejoined the girls at the top of "Fairy Hill". As soon as I arrived, Lucy stood up, ready to leave. Clara immediately followed suit, and we all made our way slowly back down the hill. I walked behind the girls as they descended slowly. I could see Lucy was still visibly upset, and Clara was clinging to her arm, gently comforting her.

Once out of the cool protection of the woodland, we were exposed to the full heat of the sun, which was surprisingly warm by Scottish standards.

Another adventure in fairyland over, and I braced myself for my inevitable return to the busy modern world. I felt a twinge of sadness but my thoughts then drifted towards Lucy who would probably be glad to see the back of September the 12th for another year.

I acknowledge that September 12th is the day after "The Twin Towers" tragedy; and I would just like to take this opportunity to send my sincere condolences to the families who lost loved ones on that terrible day.

CH8 "Salamander Day" 19.09.09

In the unseen world around us there are reputed to be many invisible beings at work; like the cogs and wheels of an old clock, whirring and spinning independently. They are all hidden from view; all of them part of "That Grand Design" which is that ornate "Old Time Piece" we affectionately call Mother Earth: Our old "Grandmother Clock"; Earth, gently "ticks" away, year after year, century after century; and is expected to keep on "ticking", no matter how many "spanners" we humans throw into "Her works".

I'm now going to play the part of "The Clockmaker" and describe one of the "tiny cogs" that "ticks" away quietly on Planet Earth: This "tiny cog" is known as "The Salamander".

The common name for "The Salamander" is "FIRE"; and fire is very painful to our human bodies if we come into direct contact with its red and orange flames (Materialists talk about "animate" and "inanimate" objects; believing that some objects are "dead", or totally devoid of life. Spiritually-minded people, on the other hand, believe that life exists EVERYWHERE, and what we call "physical matter" is constructed from a wide diversity of "Spirit

Beings" of varying complexities; each with their own individual tasks to perform. One of these simplest "beings" is called an "Elemental": Earth, Air, Wind, and of course FIRE; are all part of this "Elemental" Group).

The "Salamander" has very elastic properties and it can contract or expand at lightning speeds: If you study a naked flame you will see the movements of the red and orange "Salamanders" as they wander and flicker their merry dance (Please children; always be supervised by a responsible adult when doing this).

That was a brief description of "The Salamander", and without meaning to sound melodramatic, I'd like to tell you how these tiny but extremely volatile "beings" almost put an end to "The Treeheads" forever: Things were to become so explosive between Lucy and I that she threatened to cut all ties with me FOR GOOD! Hence, our book may have ended up unfinished; lying forgotten in a dusty old attic for centuries.

But, thankfully, we survived!

Now on to our adventure...

It was one of these cool but sunny days; typical of a Scottish autumn and, to be honest, perfect for me. It was ideal walking weather and the three of us set off in good spirits, just grateful to be fit enough to enjoy the idyllic scenery.

Lucy was grinning from earlobe to earlobe:

"I feel great!" she beamed. "On a scale of 1 to 10 I'm at my max today. How do you people feel?"

Neither Clara nor I could boast a 10, but we both agreed to feeling about 8 each; which was good for me. However, as we approached Aberfoyle, the grey skies were beginning to descend on us but this didn't dampen our spirits in the least.

As we crossed the old hump-backed bridge, I noticed the waters had receded and the river was so still; casting perfect reflections of the surrounding trees. Occasionally, small ripples would break the surface and the reflections of the trees would shimmer and tremble- the calm before the storm?

While we were walking past the houses on our right, Lucy spotted a gentleman in the distance she seemed to recognize:

"See that guy: He's a local man and he suffers from colour-blindness: He actually thought his car was orange and I had to lay an orange fruit on top of his car bonnet to prove to him it was red!"

On approaching the gentleman; as he was just about to jump into his red car, I jokingly shouted out: "I see you're taking the orange car to work today."

He wasn't happy with my comment and mumbled something disagreeable back in my direction. I felt a twinge of regret as I hadn't meant to offend the man, but I'd already said it and couldn't take it back. Lucy couldn't help herself though and let out a huge snort of laughter which didn't help matters.

Clara, however, just walked on, pretending to ignore my thoughtless but genuinely innocent comment. We continued on our way past the small pig farm with the well-kept New Zealand kune kune pigs. They were so cute and grunted hungrily as we passed by. It seemed they could smell the red strawberries I was carrying so I doubled back; parting with a couple of my precious cargo. Their pen was already littered with pieces of fruit; mainly large oranges that the pigs had hardly touched. We said our goodbyes to the pigs and headed off- first stop Robert Kirk's cemetery.

The gates were closed on our arrival and Clara was the first to open them. A loud squealing sound was heard as metal rubbed against metal. Studying the blacksmith's handy work for the first time, I noticed that both gates were decorated with ornate iron lions.

Once inside the graveyard, even I could feel a distinct change in the atmosphere:

"Is it just my imagination, or is this place more peaceful and tranquil than usual?" I announced. Both girls unanimously agreed, and as we approached Robert Kirk's Gravestone, Lucy let out an exclamation of relief:

"Look: the flowers I planted on my last visit are still here; intact!"

Clara and I both gave each other a smile of relief.

We then wandered over to Robert Kirk's grave. Each of us knew he wasn't far away, unseen, but very much alive in spirit at least. Today, I felt no urge to leave the cemetery in quite so much of a hurry. Neither did the girls, so we all sauntered out slowly, as if time itself had stood still.

Rejoining the meandering gravel path, we gently ambled past the old blue cottage on our right. Everything smacked of autumn today: the leaves on the trees were crimson red; tapering to oranges and browns. Small birds flitted about the gardens, spoilt for choice by the abundance of ripe red fruit that swelled from the trees and bushes. Directly in front of us, a Horse-Chestnut Tree was now shedding its bounty of fruit onto the path, and I gazed at the horse chestnuts as they gleamed like freshly polished shoes- instantly transporting me back to my youth when I used to play "conkers".

We were in no hurry to reach the summit of "Fairy Hill" today as the scenery was so breathtaking but soon, "Grozwald's Rock" would be looming in the distance:

"Can you see him; is he there?" Lucy asked Clara excitedly, as we approached "The Rock".

Before Clara could squeeze out an answer, the colour suddenly drained from Lucy: "I've come over all dizzy," she moaned.

"Grozwald is standing behind us all just now," announced Clara simultaneously. Turning around quickly, I waved at the empty space where I assumed the goblin would be standing.

"He waved back at you," Clara reassured me, as Lucy stood laughing out loud at my antics. But it wasn't just Grozwald who was there to meet us that day:

"I can see another goblin standing on "The Rock" just now," Clara exclaimed: *"I think it's Grozwald's wife: She's got a nicer face than Grozwald; with softer eyes that taper to the side. She's wearing a low-cut diagonal dress which looks like it's made from cheesecloth and, unlike Grozwald, who only has a few hairs on his forehead and chin, she's got long black shiny hair that frames her shoulders."* Clara then suddenly degenerated into "Grozwaldspeak":

"Yes- That my wife- She called Gorlinda."

"She sounds gorgeous," I joked. "I think I've fallen in love."

"Gorlinda didn't like that comment Adrian: She looks visibly shocked and upset by what you just said," Clara informed me.

I immediately apologized.

"Can I take a photograph of her," asked Lucy.

"She says "yes" and will try to "brighten herself up" for the picture," replied Clara- *"Gorlinda's getting impatient. She's starting to tap her right foot in irritation; waiting for you to take the shot,"* Clara informed Lucy.

This only served to make Lucy even more flustered. Eventually though, the shot was taken.

"Gorlinda's now raising her arms in the air and shouting

"Eureka"," described Clara- Well, Lucy and I just looked at each other and roared with laughter at Clara's description.

"Gorlinda has just waved goodbye and has disappeared into the woodland. Grozwald has just hopped up onto "The Rock" behind her; and is following her."

Lucy and I both waved emphatically at "The Rock", our faces beaming.

As we entered the woodland at the start of "The Fairy Trail", Lucy began complaining of chest pain and even I guessed that the spirit of Robert Kirk must be around her. Then she began belching uncontrollably:

"Burrp... I can feel Robert around me... Burrp... Burrp," burped Lucy, sounding slightly uneasy.

Clara confirmed that what Lucy was feeling at that moment was correct: Robert was indeed in very close proximity. This seemed to pacify a visibly uncomfortable Lucy and her posture began to soften almost immediately.

"Ooh, I can see faces everywhere today," Clara gasped. *"This place is full; even the tree spirits are showing themselves!"*

As we were walking up "Fairy Hill", I was suddenly overcome

with emotion. I felt so humbled in the presence of this magical place, and I silently thanked the fairies for allowing me to be part of this wonderful adventure. Clara continued expounding her exquisite visions as we ascended the winding path:

"The trees are firing "golden healing arrows" at us just now. It's not just the usual "golden drops"- we are being bombarded! Oh, and there are tiny wee figures in the surrounding woodland; they're smaller than "Action Men" and their colours vary from greens, to browns, to yellows. And there's that white "fairy horse" again- it's going too fast- I think the rider was wearing a brown cloak as he rushed by."

On approaching the summit of "Fairy Hill", the silence was broken by the sound of a dog barking in the distance...

"I heard that dog barking at the same spot on a previous visit", insisted Lucy. We had all heard the dog but I just put it down to coincidence. It sounded to me like a regular bark from a standard pet and I thought nothing more of it.

"This path was made by natural running water," continued Clara, as the path began to plateau out.

"No it wasn't." I assured Clara. "This looks like it's been made by "The Forestry Commission"."

"This is not the original path up to "Fairy Tree". Robert Kirk used to take other paths up here. The "Fairy Tree"' we visit WASN'T the main tree of worship. There was another somewhere, but I don't know where..."

Clara's trance-like speech was cut short when I spotted a small creature darting across the path ahead of us. Blocking its escape route, I stooped down to pick it up: "Look everyone!" I exclaimed. "It's a salamander!"

Clara took the creature gently from my open palm and examined it closely: *"It's not a salamander; it's just a common newt."* With that, she turned it over onto its back, revealing an orange belly.

"But the newt is related to the salamander, I'm sure of it," I insisted.

Clara then freed the creature to continue its brief life's journey.

"The Fairy Circle" was deserted when we eventually arrived on the summit so we all sat down on broken logs which were randomly strewn about the place. I opened my box of cheese and tomato sandwiches.

Clara, however, was too connected to her surroundings to think about her stomach, and began sharing another fascinating vision with us both:

"There were twelve people here recently standing in a circle, clad in red hooded cloaks with orange robes underneath, conducting some sort of ritual to do with "FIRE". I can see their hands raised upwards facing "Fairy Tree"... Wait... I can also see another person standing outside "The Circle". His hood is turned upwards, while the rest have theirs down- whatever that means? That makes THIRTEEN: A Sacred Number!"

(I would just like to explain to everyone that autumn is a season characterized by reds and oranges: Red and orange are "low vibration" colours; indicating that the energies on this planet are waning as the plants ripen, wither and die. Autumn signifies death and regeneration: "Fire" is red and orange, and can result in death and regeneration).

Now back to Clara...

"This is a sacred mound." continued Clara. *"Many religious societies came here a long time before Robert Kirk. They came here from far and wide to this ancient land known as Scotland."*

"Why so sacred?" I asked in the humble tone of a small schoolboy.

"It's all symbolism," Clara answered: *"The very act of climbing to the top of this mound is a symbol of humanity aspiring to higher and greater achievement."* Just at that moment, a robin red-breast appeared in a bush close by- maybe attracted by my sandwiches. I threw a piece of sandwich towards the bushes which initially startled the bird, as it retreated quickly into the woods. However, it returned soon after to claim its bounty. As the robin was amusing us all with its antics by nearly nose-diving into the bushes with the weight of food in its beak, Clara recommenced with her visions:

"There are golden healing drops coming down from "Fairy Tree" just now, covering us all."

I opened the cartons of strawberries and blackberries with good intentions, but couldn't help popping a couple into my mouth: "It's okay folks, I'm leaving the rest for the fairy folk," I reassured everyone.

"Too late," Clara informed me, *"I just saw a little silvery-grey hand reaching into the tub and helping itself."*

"Now, now!" I scolded; half-jokingly. "Have a wee bit of patience and let me put them on a plate first."

"Oh Adrian, it was torture for these poor wee creatures; watching you munching on the fruit. One of them just couldn't wait!" explained Clara.

Getting the message, I quickly wiped the "fairy plate" and hurriedly dropped the fruit onto it, watching the berries spill over onto the ground.

"They can't wait. Look at them!" Clara exclaimed (But we couldn't see a thing, could we?)

Lucy grabbed her camera and took a photo of the plate, hoping to catch a ghostly image, but even the camera couldn't see what the amazing Clara could see.

"The fruit's gone," announced Clara, but the plate was still bulging with the physical berries: The fairies had eaten the "essence" though, as Robert Kirk had described in his writings.

"I wonder what they taste like after the "essence" has been eaten?" enquired Lucy; popping one of the strawberries into her mouth.

"DON'T EAT IT!" I shouted half-seriously; remembering what might have become of Robert Kirk when he ate fairy food. But it was too late: Lucy had already swallowed the strawberry. I waited for a few minutes in anticipation, to see if Lucy would suddenly disappear in a puff of smoke, but thankfully she didn't.

Tentatively, I placed one of the "essence-depleted" strawberries into my mouth, chewing slowly, swilling the juice around in my mouth, as I tried to detect any subtle differences in taste:

"These strawberries taste exactly like they did BEFORE the "wee elf kids" took the "essence" and, not only that, I'm still here in one piece, and haven't disappeared into fairyland!"

"Don't be silly!" scolded Lucy; taking me seriously. "That's only supposed to happen when WE EAT THEIR FOOD!"

I continued munching, satisfied that I was out of immediate danger: "That's amazing!" I exclaimed between mouthfuls: "there's no difference in taste. I'll tell you something, I would never have suspected a thing if the elves had been eating my dinner!" With that, the girls let out a hoot of laughter.

Clara then stood up suddenly and intuitively laid her hands on "Fairy Tree":

"I have a rush of images flooding into my mind just now of

EVERYONE who has touched, made wishes at, or danced around this tree. Make the most of these quiet afternoons in this enchanted place because things will never be quite the same here again. In the future I can see this place teeming with tourists, and the elves will be driven underground."

My heart sank at the thought of this sacred place being commercialized and turned into some sort of "adventure playground": "I hope it isn't anything to do with our book?" I asked, hesitantly.

"It's not the book," Clara reassured me. *"It's the film that's just come out. It will create a huge surge of interest but hopefully it'll all die-down eventually."*

Clara sat back down with us and we relaxed in this tranquil, unspoiled place. Maybe these would be the last harmonious and peaceful days spent here, so we savoured them all the more. However, we were so engrossed in our picturesque surroundings that we quite forgot the time. It suddenly dawned on me that I'd made arrangements to pick up my daughter:

"What time do you make it girls?" I asked in a panic. "My watch says just after 2pm. Oh no, I promised I would fetch my daughter at 3pm. I'll be struggling to get back to Falkirk for 3 o'clock!"

We all checked our watches and, for some unknown reason, we were all four minutes apart. That had the effect of panicking me even more; so with barely a goodbye, I began hurriedly making my way down "Fairy Hill", gesturing in agitation for the girls to follow. As I descended rapidly, I could hear the girls in hot pursuit. The path, however, had become extremely unstable due to a combination of previous heavy rainfall, and the soil itself having a high stone content: It felt like we were walking on marbles at times. Suddenly, I heard a sickening groan behind me, and turned round just in time to see poor Clara falling heavily, with one leg trapped underneath her in a very awkward position. I've been a registered nurse for nearly twenty years and have seen some horrific falls resulting in severe fractures, but I can assure you this was as bad as I'd seen. I rushed back up the hill as poor Clara lay on her back with her right leg badly twisted underneath her. Routinely, I tested for possible head injury by looking for signs of blood from the back of her head, nose and ears. Happy that there were no immediate signs of head injury, Lucy and I tentatively turned Clara onto her left side, both fearing the worst. Clara then gingerly straightened out her previously trapped leg on my instruction and then I asked her to slowly rotate her leg clockwise, then anti-clockwise. She grimaced as she carried out my requests but, to both Lucy's and my amazement, Clara miraculously seemed to have escaped serious injury, apart from the middle finger of her left hand which was dripping blood. Lucy and I slowly assisted Clara to her feet and before long she was limping independently. We both hugged her with sheer delight and relief. I was the first to speak:

"You know something Clara: I've seen numerous falls in my career as a nurse and I can usually tell by the way a person falls whether it'll result in a fracture or not. Yours was one of the most awkward I've seen and I would have put money on you having a leg break of some kind. How you escaped with only a finger cut, I'll never know!"

Lucy nodded in agreement: "Isn't it strange that the Americans call autumn "Fall" and that's exactly what you've had Clara."

Poor wee Clara wasn't "out of the woods" yet, so to speak, as she was hobbling badly. The contorted look on her face suggested she'd torn ligaments or something, at the very least!

"Don't you think you should get an x-ray when you get back?" I suggested. "You certainly can't drive. Look, I'll do the driving. I'm in a bit of a hurry anyway."

The girls reluctantly agreed but didn't appear very enthusiastic when I mentioned the word "hurry"- and hurry I did. There's a lot of truth in the saying "more haste- less speed", and I soon found myself stuck behind a slow moving "people carrier". The occupants were obviously out for a leisurely, scenic drive. My thoughts at that moment were purely selfish, I'm ashamed to admit, and I was desperately "tail-gating"; looking for an opportunity to overtake on what is a narrow winding road with numerous blind corners.

Lucy was sitting in the back becoming increasingly upset, until eventually she began sobbing, demanding that I stop.

Quickly spotting a lay-by on my left, I brought the car to a sudden abrupt halt, and sat silently grumping. Clara seemed to anticipate an argument brewing between Lucy and me, so she suggested driving the remainder of the journey while we both cooled down.

I quickly gathered my senses though and held out a hand of

apology to Lucy, which she thankfully accepted. Poor Clara took the wheel for the rest of the journey. I don't know how she managed to drive us all home with her painful ankle but she did.

Incidentally, from an astrological point of view, both Lucy and I are both "fire signs"; Aries and Sagittarius, respectively.

Clara was born under Pisces; a "water sign", and had attempted to act as a mediator between "The Ram" and "The Archer".

Eventually the "FIRE" was quenched by the "WATER", but it could so easily have taken hold, consuming everything in its path and setting "The Treeheads" ablaze!

"THE GROZWALD"

"THE GORLINDA"

"SIPPIT", "LIPPIT" & "DIPPIT"

CAN YOU SEE THIS TREE'S OLD FACE?

CH9 Walking the "right" path 24.10.09

"Lucy has cancelled," I explained to Clara over the phone.

"Can you blame her?" Clara shouted. "Look at it out there; it's teeming with rain!"

I was determined the weather wasn't going to spoil my intended trip though, so I quickly thought of a "carrot" I could dangle in front of Clara's nose: "You got great college results recently… What if I fill up your car with petrol and we can go for a drive up to Aberfoyle? Then I'll take you to the café for a meal and, if the weather improves, we can walk up "Fairy Hill"?"

Clara was a poor student so I figured she'd find this offer difficult to resist.

"Well, that's very kind of you", she replied, "but this will cost you a small fortune."

"That's my business", I reassured her, secretly relieved that she'd given-in without a fight. So we headed off in Clara's wee car and arrived in Aberfoyle for midday.

The rain was pouring diagonally in sheets as we sat in the café eating our tasty meals. My heart sank as I stared out of the window at the perpetual downpour, silently praying to God to give us some respite. Clara must've seen the disappointment etched on my face and gave me a reassuring but exasperated smile; resigning herself to the squelching journey ahead. I smiled back with a mixture of relief and gratitude.

As we commenced our walk, the rain was so heavy it felt as if we were literally wading through torrents of water, and we stopped, only very briefly, to throw a couple of strawberries to the kune kune pigs.

"It's "The Trossachs Mushroom Festival" today," I explained to Clara, showing her a brochure I'd picked up in the café.

Eventually, we arrived at "Grozwald's Rock", and Clara immediately spotted Grozwald, but there was no sign of his wife and kids:

"Grozwald has just jumped off his rock and is running round your leg just now," she informed me.

"That's strange, because just before you said that I felt a sudden twinge in my left leg: maybe the two are related?" I guessed.

"Now he's pointing to your bag with the strawberries in it and asking, "Where's mine?"" Clara continued.

I felt a sudden surge of embarrassment: "But Grozwald, you said last time that you only eat the berries and plants that grow locally."

"He's now laughing and says he was only joking," Clara reassured me.

I let out a belly laugh: "You certainly had me fooled that time Grozwald!"

"He's clutching a bunch of white flowers in between his long bony fingers now and holding them out to you as a gift," continued Clara. After she'd shown me exactly where he was standing, I walked over to him, bent down, and mimed taking the invisible flowers; opening my bag and then placing them gently inside (I can assure you readers that I had previously checked in every direction for the psychiatrist out walking his dog before I did this).

"Ha Ha... He's now prancing up and down on one foot at a time in sheer delight, saying: "You first human ever to take gift off Grozwald!"" repeated Clara.

I felt very honoured and returned his gesture with a heart-felt thank you.

"Can I ask Grozwald a question?"

"Go ahead," replied Clara.

"Grozwald, is it just you and your family that have lived on that rock or does its history go back further?"

"No- Rock goes back further- Was my fore-fathers," answered Grozwald; through Clara.

"Did your fore-fathers die?" I enquired further.

"No- Didn't die- Ascended," was Grozwald's reply.

"Now he wants us to follow him up "Fairy Hill". He says there's a surprise waiting for us at the top," Clara continued (This immediately made me suspicious. After all, we were dealing with a kingdom of beings that were for the most part unknown to humanity and could be, according to some books I'd read, quite emotionally unpredictable).

However, I shook off my suspicions and decided to go with it:

"That's fine; we were headed up there anyway so what the heck," I grinned.

So we continued onwards and upwards with Clara informing me that Grozwald was running ahead of us, appearing quite animated, sometimes on two feet and, at others, on all fours. While we were trudging up a part of "Fairy Hill" with a steeper incline to it, Clara could see lots of small brown creatures scurrying away as we approached. Clara figured the reason they were running away was because they knew she could see them.

I forged ahead up "Fairy Hill", leaving Clara dragging behind me in the distance but, as I turned round to check on her progress, I could see her suddenly enveloped in a subtle mist. Just at that precise moment she began sharing a vision:

"I can hear a rumble; like lots of horses' hooves... wait a minute... they aren't horses; they look like small deer but they're being jockeyed like horses, with riders on their backs. Now there's a high-pitched sound- like "HIYA": the way a jockey would speak to his animal or something."

Clara then suddenly had an enlightening revelation: *"This is not "The True Path". These trees didn't used to be here. There used to be a separate path intersecting with the path we have now."*

Well, I was beginning to wish we were on the original path just now because this one was blocked by a very large fallen branch which must have crashed down in the recent high winds we'd been having. It was too heavy to move by hand so I waited for Clara to catch up with me and lifted her over, scrambling over myself shortly afterwards.

On approaching the summit, Clara could hear Grozwald excitedly saying: "The Adrian is coming and "The Goddess" is with him"; obviously referring to the name printed on the side of Clara's bag, and not Clara herself (Clara had the word "goddess" written on the side of her bag in large red lettering). Nervously, I slowly and gingerly approached the summit, peering cautiously ahead, wary of Grozwald's "surprise"!

However, there were no obvious "surprises" to be seen anywhere on the top of "Fairy Hill" when we arrived: No fairy banquets, no crystal goblets overflowing with ruby red wine and delicious fairy food. You let us down big time Grozwald but we forgive you.

Instead, my eyes were greeted by nothing less than complete carnage: torn and twisted branches felled by the recent gale- maybe this was Grozwald's idea of a surprise but it certainly wasn't mine!

Clara arrived shortly after me and stared at the mess: *"Nature goes on,"* she stated; her wise words resounding from deep within.

"Do you see that over there?" I asked, pointing to "the mist" that clung to the trees like smoke in the distance.

The crystals in Clara's hand squeaked as she held on to them more tightly as she stared in the same direction:

"I can see lots of "fairy animals" but they're just shapes. The trees are shutting down for winter... it's time to sleep. The elves are helping the trees to prepare for the shutdown."

It was now becoming very damp on top of "Fairy Hill" and, although the foliage from the trees provided some cover, the relentless rain was beginning to drip slowly through the green canopy above us. Clara and I were beginning to feel very water-logged!

"Right," I said in a soldierly like manner, "let's get the strawberries out, then we'll go home. Wiping the "fairy plate" with a handkerchief, I quickly piled on the strawberries, laying them next to "Fairy Tree". One rolled off the plate and I popped it into my mouth, chewing hurriedly, and spitting out the stalk.

"There's a whole load of elves; adults and children, standing with their hands out flat, pointed towards you. They were covering you in a golden healing energy as you were laying out the strawberries but they screwed-up their faces in disgust when you spat out that

stalk," Clara informed me.

I turned around quickly to face them and apologized sincerely: "Sorry folks, I hope I didn't get anyone in the eye. I'll have to be more careful in future." But Clara wasn't finished yet:

""Fairy Tree" is using the same golden light as the elves were using and has formed a protective dome around us both just now. We're now surrounded in a dome of pure golden energy!"

"Well that's amazing but, to be honest, I don't feel any different-maybe I'll feel it when I get home. Thanks anyway elves and tree," I added as an afterthought.

"That was their parting-gift to us both Adrian. The elves are leaving and saying their goodbyes," continued Clara.

"For how long?" I enquired, with genuine sadness.

"An elf is holding up one finger just now which means, for one season- back in spring," interpreted Clara.

"Can I ask them a few questions before they go?" I pleaded.

"You pick your times Adrian- they're dwindling fast- be quick!" hurried Clara.

"Do you mind me writing this book? I mean, I'm not doing it for financial gain. I've never wanted to be rich, just comfortable," I reassured them.

"Some of them aren't happy about it but they know your motives aren't for personal gain and that's why they're communicating with us- Oh, and don't worry, you'll never be rich," assured Clara.

To be honest, I was a wee bit disappointed at the prospect of never being wealthy, but the main reason for writing this book was to demonstrate to everyone that this beautiful planet is teeming with life, visible and invisible, and we must learn to treat Mother Earth with the utmost respect! It's time to get off my soapbox and back to the story...

Clara informed me that the elves were leaving and Grozwald was standing facing them; bowing in respect, with his right hand placed across his stomach.

"The Royal Party have stayed behind and have one last thing to say before they leave," announced Clara:

"They say that the year 2012 will be a year filled with a series of natural disasters, but through lessons learned people will ultimately become more spiritual."

Then they were gone and all we were left with was Grozwald; sniffing the physical shells of the strawberries after the elves had eaten their "essence".

I could feel the emptiness of the place now. It was like that desolate feeling we all have after an important birthday party; when all our friends have gone home and all we're left with is material gifts, cardboard boxes and wrapping paper: the "empty-shell" reminders of their warmth and love. In this case the "empty-shell" reminders were the strawberries themselves; soon to be devoured by the woodland creatures after we'd left. As I sat in the still emptiness of the place my thoughts drifted towards the absent Lucy:

"It's a pity Lucy isn't here to receive her healing. I'm sure she could do with it just now."

Clara then began speaking again:

""Fairy Tree" is telling Lucy to go to an oak tree before its leaves fall, and she will get her healing."

We both thanked the grand old "Fairy Tree" and began our descent back down the hill with Grozwald in hot pursuit, apparently with both arms swinging by his sides as he imitated my walk.

As we continued our gentle meander down the hill the scenery was becoming strangely unfamiliar...

"This doesn't look like our usual route!" Clara announced, echoing my sentiments exactly. For a moment I began to become a wee bit concerned. I'd read in books about people who had gone missing for weeks and returned with stories of being lost in the world of fairy- and that was the ones that came back to tell the tale! What about the ones that DON'T? Then I became more logical, convincing myself we'd just deviated from the main path.

"This was the original path that Robert used to take," Clara enlightened me. *"The other path that we've walked, up until now, was made by "The Forestry Commission"."*

"But why? This is a much more pleasant walk. The slopes meander gently downwards and there seems to be plenty of places to stop and take in the scenery, plus you have a better view of the surrounding countryside- it doesn't make sense," I pondered, genuinely perplexed. "Anyway, they must have had their reasons, I suppose- but that apart- what amazes me is that you were talking about "The Right Path" as we were struggling up the tourist path that "The Forestry Commission" had made, and now we find ourselves on that very path!"

"That's the power of spirit!" announced Clara.

That just about summed things up: it was indeed "the power of spirit", and I had experienced for probably the first time just how powerful "spirit" could be!

I was, however, very relieved when we finally exited the woods and found the old familiar countryside we were used to. Sounds silly, I know, but who knows what lies hidden in the lands of the fairy?

By the way, to be on the safe side I turned my bag inside out, just to make sure that Grozwald's flowers weren't going back home with me to Falkirk. Let's be honest, they would have clashed with the decor in my sitting room anyway.

"What happened to you?" I grumbled; exasperated. "It's nearly two o'clock. By the time we get to Aberfoyle it'll be dark!"

"I know it will. My daughter held me up; wanting me to take her to Glasgow," explained an apologetic Clara. *"Anyway, you know what they say: "God's timing is perfect"."*

I calmed down eventually. She was right: God's timing was indeed perfect. Maybe we were supposed to go up to "Fairy Hill" when it was dark and spooky- who knows? "Anyway, we'd better hurry: Lucy's waiting for us at Falkirk Retail Park," I said.

Lucy had a look of excitement and anticipation when we arrived; which was understandable, as she'd been with her boyfriend for several weeks and seemed desperate to return to fairyland. By the time we arrived in Aberfoyle, though, the light was already beginning to fade and this wasn't helped by the cloud cover.

Lucy, however, jumped out of the car like an excited schoolgirl, visibly overjoyed at being back after such a long sojourn:

"I'm away to get something from the shops. I'll meet you both on top of "Fairy Hill"," she squealed.

I was itching to get up to "Grozwald's Rock" before it got dark because I knew how much the little goblins hated the dark; so poor wee Clara was literally marched up the path, the kune kune pigs, graveyard, and old cottage were just a blur as we rushed past them. The pigs were sniffing at the black grapes I was carrying as we hurried by; but that's all they got, a sniff!

When we arrived at "The Rock" Clara reassured me that the whole family; Grozwald, his wife and kids were all waiting for us.

On my way up the path I'd been munching on some of the grapes and was "machine-gunning" the surrounding countryside with the pips. By the time we arrived, I'd eaten half of the grapes already and gingerly offered the wee goblin family what was left of them:

"These grapes are absolutely gorgeous. Can I leave a few of them on top of "The Rock" for Grozwald and Co?" I suggested.

"That's fine- Thank you," Clara replied; being the perfect goblin advocate.

"Careful of the pips," I warned the goblin family.

"What's pips?" Clara asked in perfect "Grozwaldspeak".

"Oh sorry- the other word for them is seeds," I explained.

"Grozwald says: "I like the grape a lot", and is holding one in his hand at this moment; munching on it," described Clara. *"Gorlinda isn't eating her grape: she seems too ladylike to want to be seen spitting out the seeds in public, and also doesn't want to eat with her hands as she sometimes uses them for walking as well,"* Clara continued.

"Oh the curse of being a lady," I sighed. "I'm so glad I don't walk on my hands as well: Imagine going into a burger restaurant after walking through some of the yucky stuff that litters our city streets?"

"Okay Adrian, you've said enough," winced Clara.

Changing the subject, I moved on to the baby goblins: "What do Grozwald's babies think of my tasty treats?" I enthused.

"Mixed responses," replied Clara: *"Sippit is sucking the juice from her grape, Lippit is doing exactly that, and Dippit has thrown hers away!"*

"Ah well, we can't please all of the goblins all of the time, can we?" I conceded; borrowing heavily from a famous speech made by some American president in the distant past, I think.

"At least it's a better response than I got from my strawberry offering," I added. Clara nodded in agreement.

"Would the family like me to bring them up some more grapes next time I drop by?" I generously suggested.

"Apart from this "one-off" gift which Grozwald thanks you for, he's generally not allowed to take gifts from anyone. His job is to guard the entrance to this place," Clara explained. *"He guards this place from creatures of other domains; and that's his job!"*

"Okay then, what happens then if one of these "creatures of other domains" tries to force its way past him?" I quizzed.

"He can quickly summon help and forcibly remove the unwanted creature," replied Clara.

"Right, so he can get the other elves... sorry... goblins to help him remove the undesirable from the area," I concluded.

"Yes," Clara replied. *"Oh and by the way, he's not very happy at you calling him an elf. He's standing with his hands on his hips staring disapprovingly at you just now."*

"I'm genuinely sorry Grozwald," I said in a groveling fashion.

"Apology accepted," confirmed Clara.

"Grozwald says he's going to accompany us both up to "Fairy

Tree" with his three daughters," Clara informed me.

"What about his dearest wife Gorlinda?" I asked; choosing my words very carefully.

"Unfortunately, someone has to stay on guard at "The Rock"," Clara explained.

So off we headed, after waving goodbye to Gorlinda, and continued deeper into that enchanted woodland. As we slowly ambled up this gently sloping and sacred path, I was treated to a vivid description of the goblin families' antics as they followed us, and could picture them in my mind's eye: *the animated Grozwald and his drooling babies dancing around us as we walked up the original path to "Fairy Tree"*; and what a picturesque path it was, meandering through grassy clearings with a magnificent view of the hills surrounding the old town:

"Yes- Yes- Yes- This is True Path!'" confirmed Clara; mirroring Grozwald's excitable nature and immigrant style of English: *"Don't hinder long"* which I think meant; don't stay around too long because the light is fading and the "Creatures of the Dark" would soon be out!

As we continued upwards, enjoying the relaxed climb, Clara

burst out into more "Grozwaldspeak":

"The Lucy coming": I turned round to see Lucy in the distance, slogging up "The Forestry Commission" path.

We were nearing the summit now and the ground in front of us was covered in golden leaves which deceptively hid treacherous mud and loose stones underneath. Remembering Clara's previous sickening fall, I instinctively took a tight grip of her right shoulder as we negotiated the last part of the journey together. We had arrived on the summit before Lucy, and were approaching "Fairy Tree", when Grozwald began speaking again:

"The Lucy get healing from oak tree- The Lucy go fast!"... No sooner had these words left Clara's lips when the strong and fit Lucy arrived on the scene, bristling with energy and enthusiasm.

Despite the three of us now being together on the top of "Fairy Hill" for the first time in a quite a while, there was a distinct feeling of emptiness about the place, not helped by the bare, leafless "tree skeletons":

"This place feels devoid of life: you can tell the elves have departed," I commented, with obvious hindsight.

Clara suddenly began speaking:

"The trees are going into slumber and when the last leaf falls; they will all go to sleep." It was haunting and poetic when she spoke like this but she soon returned to sobriety, obviously distracted by something she could see around her that the rest of us couldn't. Fascinated by what she was peering at, Lucy and I asked in unison what she could see:

"There are creatures that look like rabbits hopping around this place, except they're much larger than normal rabbits, and they're grey/white in colour," explained Clara.

"How big are these things?" I asked with genuine fascination, and with a smirk of amusement at Clara's descriptions.

"As big as dogs!" came back her reply.

So, while Clara and I were having our "giant bunny talk", Lucy was performing her exotic rituals around "Fairy Tree"; which included gyrating body movements, and the ritualistic sowing of seeds.

I decided to do my tourist on the top of "Fairy Hill" bit and wandered off to read the latest wishes posted on all the trees in the circle. There were little coloured flags with an endearing message: "In loving memory of .... Happy 40th Birthday, Much

Love X"... and there was also a letter and coin from further afield; with a photo of a young man. The coin had "50 Forint" stamped on it and, as I wandered around aimlessly, Clara began speaking again:

"A select few elves; hand chosen by The Elf Queen, come back here on Halloween to make sure that no harm comes to this place."

"What happens to the rest?" I enquired.

"They live in an underground city which is like perpetual summer," explained Clara.

While Clara and I were speaking together, Lucy was standing in the periphery of "The Fairy Circle", closer to the surrounding woodland, when she suddenly interrupted us both:

"I'm sure I could hear a "low growling" sound in the distance. It didn't sound very inviting, I can tell you!"

As Lucy was speaking, Clara informed us that Grozwald was becoming increasingly agitated as the darkness was drawing in: "When the elves are away "The Creatures of the Dark" draw in closer, and they're known to "growl and hiss"!" she added. *I could suddenly feel a slight pain in my left leg, and was relieved when Clara informed me it was maybe just a sensation in my "etheric body" caused by Grozwald and his kids standing right behind me-to my left* (The human "etheric body" is supposed to be constructed of finer substance than our physical body and is invisible to the naked eye, and, according to ancient beliefs, our physical body is constructed on top of our "etheric body"; so our "etheric body" acts much like a "framework" for our physical body. The elves, fairies and goblins don't have physical bodies; only "etheric bodies". We humans, supposedly, have both).

The darkness was descending fast and I could sense Grozwald's agitation, or maybe it was my own, I don't know. I just had this sudden urge to turn on my heels and run down "Fairy Hill" as fast as my legs would take me, but I held my nerve. To make matters worse, Clara began peering nervously through the trees into the distance:

"I can see "black shadows" flitting from tree to tree and drawing closer by the minute- they look like "keyhole" shapes, but longer to one side," she explained.

""The Shadow People"!" I shouted out. "I saw a program on T.V. that described these things: It said they were mostly seen in graveyards at night, were a similar shape to the description you've just given, and had been seen darting from one gravestone to another in a similar fashion."

"Grozwald is nodding his head furiously as you speak; desperate to leave!" said Clara. Even Lucy, who had suggested CAMPING overnight in this place, agreed it was time for us to leave. With that, we promptly began descending "Fairy Hill"; all of us returning via the original path.

As we were walking back down the hill, Lucy began speaking: "You know something everyone, I haven't had the nausea and belching episodes I had on previous visits."

Maybe she spoke too soon because Clara suddenly began with her "Grozwaldspeak":

"The Robert with The Lucy just now," and with that, Lucy stopped next to a nearby tree and began coughing uncontrollably. The coughing fit was so severe that soon Lucy was retching next to the tree. Inadvertently though, she had stopped next to an OAK TREE that still had a few scattered green leaves attached to it:

"I can see golden droplets cascading down from the branches of this tree onto Lucy, and brightening up her "aura"," described Clara. *"With an "aura" as bright as that you'll be attracting everyone for*

miles around!" continued Clara... *"HACH HEESH NA,"* Clara then wailed, suddenly, out of the blue- then explained herself to her perplexed companions: *"This is protection for Lucy,"* she reassured us. We stood at the oak tree for a wee while; allowing time for Lucy to recover her composure, before eventually exiting the dark, mysterious wood somewhat relieved. It was surprising how light the surrounding countryside appeared once we were back out in the open.

We escorted Grozwald and his babies safely back to "The Rock", and then waved goodbye. On the way back to the car, the kune kune pigs came rushing towards us, hoping for a grape, but sadly there were none. If I'd known Dippit was going to throw hers away, I would've saved them one.

CH11 "Sliding Plates" 23.01.10

So this was our first return to fairyland as "Treeheads Together" after a busy Xmas and New Year.

Lucy was frantically making arrangements for her boyfriend's visit; trying to get her house in order. Clara was studying furiously for her degree, and I'd been in the unenviable position of moving house over the festive period, having barely recovered from the added stress and strain of it all. However, all our troubles paled into insignificance when compared to the poor Haitians who'd had their lives blighted further by a recent massive earthquake.

As we all headed off in Clara's car, we were so excited at the prospect of our first adventure of 2010. Lucy, as usual, was the liveliest of the three of us; chattering away like a budgie on the journey out:

"How do you feel on a scale of 1-10 today Lucy?" I asked her.

"A HUNDRED!" came back her emphatic reply.

Once we'd arrived in Aberfoyle, Lucy insisted on treating us all to a meal at the café, and neither Clara nor I needed much persuasion. We all shared our Xmas adventures over steaming cups of hot chocolate and iced buns before we decided, rather reluctantly, to exchange the warmth inside the café for the cold trek back up to "Fairy Hill". As soon as we set foot outside, we could all feel how cold it was, despite the overcast sky. The remnants of the recent spell of heavy snow and plummeting temperatures had resulted in black compacted ice everywhere; which was treacherous underfoot.

On route, we briefly popped into the tourist shop across the road to buy some woollen hats with ear protectors. As you've probably guessed, the hats were dark blue and white, and covered with Scottish Flags. Lucy, however, declined my generous offer of a Scottish Hat, probably on account of it clashing with her multi-coloured striped Wellingtons!

Feeling slightly better prepared, we set off over the hump-backed bridge but were immediately exposed to the full onslaught of the biting wind. The hat provided welcome protection for my poor ears though; and Clara didn't seem to care what she looked like either, as long as she was warm.

The path ahead of us was encrusted with sheets of black ice so we walked slowly and gingerly together, with Clara sandwiched tightly between us for protection; due to her recent horrific fall.

However, I soon started to regret my choice of footwear: training shoes! On this surface they were little better than ice skates, as I was to find out later. I'm sure you can imagine what a slow and treacherous walk it was today, and it seemed to take forever.

In the distance we could see the kune kune pigs, and they seemed to sense us before they could see us by the sound of their squealing and grunting. Luckily, I had a banana with me which I threw towards them. It was hungrily devoured. After such a long time away, we agreed that we should pay a visit to Robert's Grave as a token of respect.

The grass had a crispy, matted feel underfoot as we entered the cemetery, and there was a damp, mildew feeling about the place which was compounded by the cold air. The cemetery had that usual bare and barren look about it today, which was understandable due to the recent extremes of weather Scotland had been having.

"I can't feel Robert Kirk here at all today," Lucy exclaimed.

Clara agreed, stating she felt the place was completely empty and, even I, the least sensitive of all "The Treeheads" felt nothing.

"For some reason, I have the urge to touch Robert's Gravestone with my left leg," announced Lucy.

"Maybe you're helping to heal my poor leg," intuited Clara, rolling up her left trouser leg to reveal a massive bruise radiating from her ankle upwards.

"How did you do that?" Lucy and I both shouted; horrified by the huge purple and yellow mark that adorned poor Clara's leg.

"A shelf collapsed on me when I was sitting on the toilet," admitted a brave and honest Clara. We both laughed out loud and Clara joined in; seeing the humour of the situation. *"You should see the poor cat now: he jumps out of his skin at the least bit thing!"* expanded Clara.

"Was he in the loo with you at the time?" I laughed.

Clara gave me a half-smile which indicated I'd taken the joke far enough. The laughter had now died down and I was ready to leave when Clara had an unexpected vision:

"I can see lots of "white spirals" coming out of the ground just now," she suddenly remarked. *"They're starting out small, and then fanning outwards as they travel upwards."*

(Clara's vision suddenly triggered a memory of something I had read in some ghost book, years ago, about the frightening experience of a gentleman who had lived in a house overlooking an old graveyard:

One moonlit night, this particular gentleman was peering out of his bedroom window down onto the spooky old cemetery below when his eyes beheld a very eerie sight: Suddenly, a "white spiral" ascended out of the ground, followed shortly afterwards by a "black spiral". Both "spirals" then took on human form and began dancing a ghostly dance together in their morbid theatre, with this solitary, unfortunate spectator in his window seat, probably by now with very wet and soggy pyjamas, I would imagine).

I digress- back to the story:

"Now I can see loads of "spirals"!" gasped Clara. *"They're all different colours: oranges, blues, and yellows."*

I felt a twinge of envy. All I could see was a cold and unwelcoming monochrome graveyard, enveloped in a typical Scottish grey sky.

Once we'd left the cemetery, Clara informed us that the "spirals" were now beginning to diminish in number. Then, on the way out, the "eagle-eyed" Clara pointed to a half-hidden tombstone which had a carving on it that even I recognized:

"That's amazing!" I exclaimed: "It looks exactly like your description of the goblin Grozwald!"

"I can hear Grozwald saying "Hmmm- Hmmm"; as if in agreement," Clara informed us all. *"So maybe I'm not mad after all?"* Clara reassured herself.

"Do you think Lucy and I would be out on a bitterly cold day like this listening to your fascinating visions if we thought you were crazy?" I asked.

"I suppose not," Clara agreed. *"But I can't help questioning my sanity at times."*

"You're not insane- It's the rest of the world that's insane. If only we could see the world as you see it Clara: WE MIGHT THEN TREAT IT WITH A LOT MORE RESPECT!"

Once we'd established ourselves back on the main path leading to "The Fairy Trail", Lucy began belching uncontrollably: "Burrrp... Why does healing have to sound so rude?" she belched.

The cold air seemed to carry low vibration sounds well today, and crows could be heard cawing in the barren branches of distant trees. Fat wood pigeons, disturbed by our sudden presence amidst their winter solace, fluttered frantically away; the drumming sound of their beating wings accelerating as they clumsily attempted to clear the treetops.

As we passed the old blue cottage, my thoughts were suddenly with the elderly ladies inside; hoping they were warm enough on this bitterly cold day. Over to our left, the trees on "Fairy Hill" appeared in shades of grey rather than colours today; only adding to the mystery of the place.

We were now on the last part of our journey; where the ice covered path takes on an incline before it reaches the entrance to the woodland around "Fairy Hill". Here it was very slippery, and my poor choice of footwear was beginning to tell: Whilst attempting to cross the path in front of the entrance of "The Fairy Trail" my shoes began to slide uncontrollably, and I had no choice but to "skate" back down the incline of the hill using my flat soled shoes as "ice skates". All I could hear were hoots of laughter from the girls, followed by a huge round of applause. I eventually came to a stop at the bottom of the hill and Lucy shouted over:

"That was a tidy display of skating there. You did well to keep your balance. Clara and I thought you'd end up on your backside."- "Well, so did I!" came back my instant reply.

Once we finally managed to reach "Fairy Wood", Clara began speaking in "Pidgin"; or should I say "goblin" English:

""You funny man"; Grozwald says. He really thought you were going to fall," expanded Clara. *"He's standing on his rock just now, trying to make himself visible, and wants you to take a photo of him."*

Hurriedly, I took out my mobile phone camera but my ice cold hands were numb and refused to work.

"Grozwald's getting impatient," Clara pressurised me. *"He's sitting with both hands under his chin; smiling and saying: "Take Photo- Take Photo"."*

"Okay... Okay," I grumbled, further slowed down by Grozwald's pressure. Eventually, I got a shot, but couldn't see Grozwald anywhere; which I know won't surprise a lot of folk. I then handed my phone to Clara, who couldn't see him either, and I was hoping that if he was there in the photo then Clara would spot him. I was sure she could spot Grozwald in a "Goblin Identity Parade".

Finally, the three of us regrouped and tentatively trekked up

"Fairy Hill" via the original path Robert Kirk supposedly took, despite Grozwald's protestations of *"No Safe- No Safe!"* Once established on the winding path up through the wood, both girls began complaining of sudden onset nausea.

Clara said she could also see those giant "rabbit-like" creatures again scurrying about the place.

The girls' nausea eventually subsided and Lucy suddenly started powering ahead of our group like a mountain goat. Clara and I weren't feeling quite so energetic today, however, and we stopped briefly at a nearby tree to gather our breath. Clara then peered up at the trunk; entranced by another vision:

"Grozwald is hanging on to that tree and peering down at us just now."

"Where?" I asked, screwing my eyes up tight, hoping it would make some difference to my bog-standard vision. Clara pointed to the spot but as I peered closer, all I got was tree trunk. So instead of peering, I opted for speaking instead: "Was that stone carving in the cemetery one of your kind?" I asked him.

"Carving one of ancients- Like me- But not me," Clara replied on Grozwald's behalf, then began describing him; painting a

wonderful mental image for me:

"He looks like one of these "Aussie Koala Bears" just now by the way he's hanging on to that tree and peering down from behind the trunk."

Continuing my questioning, I asked Grozwald how he was able to hold on to the trunk:

"Sharp nails- Me often climb to top of trees," replied Clara; parroting the goblin.

"Why you black and blue?" Grozwald then asked Clara (He was referring to the colour of the woollen hat Clara was wearing with the Scotland flag sewn onto it.)

"Because a shelf fell on me," I quickly replied, before Clara had the chance to answer for herself.

"Grozwald doesn't understand your answer," Clara informed me; so I had to go through the laborious process of explaining to an invisible goblin that "black and blue" also means bruising; and that Clara had recently been the victim of a collapsing shelf.

"You funny man- The Lucy get present at the top of hill," Grozwald informed us through Clara; jumping suddenly from one topic to another.

By this time Lucy was way ahead of us and couldn't be seen. As Clara and I slowly ambled after her, a passing tree caught her eye:

"There looks like a sleeping man with a long beard at the bottom of that tree." Then she intuitively informed me it was a "doorkeeper"; there to protect and guard the tree over winter.

When we eventually arrived at the top of "Fairy Hill", we were greeted by a sobbing Lucy:

"What's up?" asked a concerned Clara, moving close to hug and comfort her.

"I can't breathe and my chest is very painful!" she cried.

Clara was very calm and reassuring: *"Listen Lucy, the spirit of Robert Kirk is very close to you just now. He doesn't mean to cause you distress but his aura carries the emotional pain of his heart attack and, unfortunately, you will feel that pain every time he draws close."* After she'd finished calming Lucy, Clara bent down and gathered up some of the rich, oxygenated lichen that grew in abundance in the area: *"Here, put this up to your nose and breathe in deeply: this is Grozwald's gift to you."*

"Thank you Clara and Grozwald. I really thought I had genuine heart problems for a minute," sighed a visibly relieved Lucy.

"That reminds me: I read somewhere once that people in touch with "the other side" have a higher incidence of heart attacks. Contact with "the unseen" supposedly puts greater strain on the heart. Robert Kirk was certainly in touch with "other realms" and he died suddenly on top of "Fairy Hill"," I stated in a matter-of-fact manner.

"Well, that certainly makes me feel great!" Clara replied; with an expression that suggested otherwise.

Having regained her composure, Lucy began sharing her experiences with us:

"You know earlier when I was approaching the summit of "Fairy Hill"- well I'm sure I heard a dog barking again." Before Lucy could share more information, Clara suddenly interrupted:

"I have a message from Robert Kirk for you. He says that you've seen him once. You didn't know it was him at the time but you definitely set eyes upon him." Clara continued addressing an amazed Lucy:

"Robert also insists that when your boyfriend arrives, you're forbidden to bring him up here. The energies will be too strong for

him and could be dangerous!" Lucy now appeared indignant at Clara's words, as I knew that she loved her boyfriend and had intended to visit this sacred place with him once he arrived back from working abroad.

I turned gently around to face a visibly upset Lucy and said: "We all have a "veil" lifted from us when we leave our earthly body after death; and we can see things much clearer on "the other side". Please don't ignore Robert's guidance. He obviously has a deep affection for you."

Lucy still appeared visibly disappointed, but she seemed to take Robert's advice reluctantly on board. However, she was the first to stand up and make her intentions clear that she wanted to return to the car. Clara and I followed her and, as we began our descent back down "Fairy Hill", our sympathies were still with Lucy; as we knew how much she missed her boyfriend.

Just as we were leaving, however, Clara described visions of "spirals" of many colours: greens, yellows, and purples- shooting out of the ground and disappearing into the vast sky above us:

"Robert Kirk is letting me know that the "spirals" are energy from deep inside the Earth. He says there is a huge "energy-shift"

taking place in the core of the Earth just now and there would be more huge earthquakes soon. He's also telling me that the nausea we all experienced at the bottom of "Fairy Hill" was caused by huge "magnetic shifts" taking place on this planet at the moment."

Funnily enough, on the way back down "Fairy Hill", the girls began to feel nauseous again- and so did I, but less so. *Clara said she could see many yellow "spirals" whizzing along the path and shooting straight up into the sky. After waving goodbye to Grozwald, Clara pointed towards a wooded valley between two hills:*

"I can see a distinctive yellow glow between these two hills," she announced. Unfortunately; as usual, I couldn't see the wood for the trees!

(A "fault-line" is supposed to run through this area of Scotland: A book I read made a connection between "fault-lines" and unexplained phenomena taking place in areas where "fault-lines" occur. "Ley-Lines" are supposed to be ancient routes for Mother Earth's energy; and are supposed to occur near fault-lines.)

CH12 Aberfoyle can be a "pain in the neck" 20.02.10

Lucy decided it would be easier if Clara and I met up with her in Stirling; so Clara could drive us both up to Aberfoyle from there- so that's exactly what we did.

It was a bright but cold day today; perfect for walking, and Lucy reflected the weather with her cheerful mood and brightly coloured clothes as she greeted us both warmly with smiles and hugs.

As usual, I was hogging the C.D. player in the car, but I reluctantly gave it up when Lucy insisted we all listen to a disc she'd recently bought in a shop that was having a sale in Falkirk:

"It's by a modern pop group. I bought it along with other stuff the shop was selling for discount prices. It was only when I got it home that I realized there was a song called "Aberfoyle" on it- Let's have a listen." So we did; and it was a catchy song by an obviously talented band about Robert Kirk and his encounters with the fairy folk. The band had obviously done some research into the legend because the lyrics of the song were accurate enough.

"Well that's amazing!" Clara commented, after the song had finished. *"What's the chances of you finding that C.D? I tell you: "God works in mysterious ways"!"*

We were all agreed on that one, and it seemed a good omen for our planned trip together. We listened to the rest of the songs on the disc as we drove cheerfully onwards towards that little place with the big personality.

However, as we were approaching Aberfoyle itself, Lucy began complaining of her trademark symptoms:

"I've got a pain in the right side of my neck and now in my left shoulder blade," she groaned.

"It's okay Lucy, relax," Clara reassured her, *"I'm sure it's the spirit of Robert Kirk and Aberfoyle that makes you feel this way: You obviously have a very close connection to the man and this place."* No sooner had she made her point than we found ourselves pulling up at Aberfoyle car park; Clara's "parking-angel" providing her with an ideal space for her car. The girls jumped out and they eagerly headed off towards "The Fairy Trail". I doubled back into the village to buy some provisions for the journey; as it always gives me a hearty appetite.

So, by the time I reached the kune kune pigs the girls were nowhere to be seen. I stopped briefly to watch my "bristle-covered buddies" tucking into a feast of carrots, strawberries, cucumber, and what looked like rhubarb. I was in a world of my own; contemplating the fairies, when suddenly the girls jumped out in front of me, giving me quite a fright:

"Where have you lot been?" I demanded, once I'd recovered my composure.

"We've been taking photographs of "our houses"," they replied in unison.

"But that's impossible- unless of course you've both got extremely high-powered telephoto lenses fitted to your cameras: You live miles away in Falkirk Lucy; and you live in Stirling Clara."

"Oh you are so witty- NOT," replied Lucy. "Come on up this path and look at the houses Clara and I have chosen for ourselves in the future."

So to satisfy their whims, I followed them both up the side path to look at "their houses". I preferred Clara's choice to be honest: Hers was a traditional stone built house with bags of character, where-as Lucy's was a relatively modern building, albeit with up-to-date facilities.

"Aren't you folks jumping the gun?" I laughed. "Nobody here is wealthy enough to afford such lovely places to live in as these!"

"Adrian, don't you realize that your dreams today are your realities tomorrow?" smiled Lucy (I didn't want to spoil the girls having a wee bit of a dream, did I, so I chose to say nothing, and we continued our journey together up to Robert Kirk's cemetery).

Once inside the cemetery gates, Clara produced a small hand-held video camera and began filming Robert's Tomb. She also took some film of the "goblin carving" that I mentioned in the previous chapter.

I busied myself by staring at the flowers and fauna in the place, and I noticed for what was normally a barren and bleak graveyard; somehow the place seemed pleasantly brighter today. There were flowers and plants in abundance; and I particularly noticed the small bunches of "snowdrops" dotted here and there; signaling the start of spring. "Snowdrops" were a favourite of my dear late mother, and she always pointed them out to my sister and me on the many woodland walks she took us on as kids. I quickly came out of my sentimental reminisce, however, and turned to see Lucy standing next to Robert's Gravestone, paying her usual deep respects; as if she were commiserating a close relative:

"I can feel a tingling sensation beneath my feet... wait... now it's turned into a shaking feeling!" she exclaimed.

"Well, I feel nauseous," announced Clara. *"And I can see lots of those yellow "spirals" shooting out of the ground again,"* she continued.

I decided it was time to leave, and the girls followed me out shortly afterwards. Onwards we continued up the well-trodden path towards "The Fairy Trail" as "Treeheads Together". We arrived safely at "Grozwald's Rock" without a single belch or burp from Lucy-and that was a miracle in itself!

So here we were again, standing at Grozwald's moss-covered rock. Naturally, I turned towards Clara for reassurance that he was actually standing there. She nodded with a smile, so I began addressing Grozwald politely; trusting Clara's visions implicitly.

Lucy couldn't contain herself though and erupted into howls of laughter at what must have been a very comical sight: me talking to what looked like just a lump of rock.

But Clara didn't see the funny side:

"Grozwald doesn't appreciate being laughed at," she said solemnly.

With that, Lucy apologized immediately; explaining to Clara that she was laughing at me and not Grozwald. I noticed that Lucy still refused to speak directly towards "Grozwald's Rock"- She still hadn't taken that leap of faith yet.

The apology seemed to be accepted though, because soon, Clara was talking in her usual immigrant style of English: *"Where were you last week? Me expecting you."*

"We sorry to disappoint "The Grozwald"," replied Lucy; with an obvious dig at his "Pidgin English".

I gave Lucy an icy stare. We didn't want to risk offending this goblin-it could destroy the whole book!

Grozwald seemed to pick up on Lucy's mimicking reply, but luckily, he didn't seem to be offended in any way:

"I no speak like that- That's how wife speaks," replied Grozwald; who seemed to be comparing Lucy's high-pitched female voice with his wife's: He was obviously intelligent enough to realize that Lucy was imitating him though.

I quickly changed the subject; intuitively aware of the wee goblin's sensitivity: "Grozwald, do you mind if I call you Groz?" I asked politely.

"My name not short enough already?" came back the instant reply.

Shortly afterwards, a woman appeared on the scene riding a pony, so we quickly said our goodbyes and entered Fairy Wood via the original path that Robert Kirk supposedly used to take. Ten minutes into our walk, I turned round to see Lucy struggling behind in third place. I was surprised because she normally bounded ahead like a dog chasing squirrels.

Clara then burst into more "Grozwaldspeak": *"The Lucy full."* Lucy certainly did appear "full" as she struggled to keep up with the rest of us.

"I can smell food cooking," Lucy explained, but all Clara and I could smell was the chimney smoke from houses nearby. Clara then slowed down to allow Lucy to catch up; after all, a slow amble was all that was required. It gave us time to feast our eyes on the wonderful colours that the sunlight picked out as it filtered through the trees: A carpet of moss lay around us, draped in brown, yellow and golden leaves; the moisture on their surfaces shimmering in the sharp winter sun.

As we approached the summit, Lucy began complaining of a pain in her neck again. However, the pain soon seemed to subside and she was able to continue the rest of the climb in comfort. What an unpleasant surprise awaited us though, when we eventually arrived on the summit of "Fairy Hill": "Fairy Tree" and all the other trees in "The Circle" had been stripped bare of all their gifts, wishes, and brightly coloured ribbons: They stood there, naked and vulnerable in the cold winter sun.

Clara walked over to "Fairy Tree" to examine it closely and noticed a five pointed star had been carved into its bark with the letter "M" above its northern point. Clara then began touching the trunk to try to gain some information:

"It's okay: the items taken from the trees were all placed inside a box. It wasn't done out of malice. I can now see "Fairy Tree" starting to glow a golden colour; stretching about two feet out from its trunk. Grozwald is also reassuring me that "Fairy Tree" wasn't stripped out of malice; so I think that settles things," continued Clara.

"Is Grozwald here with us just now?" enquired Lucy.

"The whole family are," replied Clara in a matter-of-fact tone.

"Why didn't you tell us?" I asked. "You know Lucy and I can't see anything. We rely on you solely as our eyes and ears!"

"Sorry folks," replied a red faced Clara, *"I sometimes assume that what I see; everyone else sees."*

"Okay then, what's happening with Grozwald and his family just now?"

"Well," replied Clara, *"Grozwald and his wife Gorlinda are sitting basking in the sun watching their kids Sippit, Lippit, and Dippit tumbling and play-fighting in the grass. Two of the kids are wearing loin cloths, and the other a dress."*

"That's better," I smiled, writing furiously whilst walking towards a violet-coloured wind chime that was tied to a fallen branch in the surrounding undergrowth. Just at that, a more assertive Clara informed me that Grozwald's kids were following me over to the wind chime.

As I sauntered slowly back over to "Fairy Tree", Clara suddenly announced that she could also see the ghost of Robert Kirk standing in front of her, very smartly dressed in a white collared shirt and a long black coat, with tails at the back. According to Clara, he was also wearing shiny black shoes, and had a large top-hat on.

"He must look like a lord!" I announced.

"Indeed he does," remarked Clara. *"Oh look! He gave me a pose when I mentioned how smart he looks,"* she smiled.

I laughed at the thought of Robert showing off his gentlemanly attire.

As for Lucy, she was sitting with her back against "Fairy Tree" with her arms and legs crossed over; soaking up the sun.

"Does anyone fancy a drink?" I asked, innocently pointing to a carton of fruit juice lying next to "Fairy Tree".

"When you mentioned "DRINK", Robert's face suddenly took on a stern appearance," laughed Clara. *"I think he thought you were referring to alcohol."*

Again, I had to chuckle at the thought of the strict Presbyterian's reaction to my innocent suggestion.

Lucy then seemed to briefly awaken from her slumber at the foot of "Fairy Tree": "You know something," she said, "I feel as if I could lie here forever: I don't want to move from this spot."

"Robert is telling me that he used to sit in exactly the same position that you are in just now; and that's where he used to read his Bible," Clara informed Lucy. *"He's now holding up his fingers... wait a minute... I think it's a 2, 5, and 7 or 258. Maybe he wants us to read the Bible: pages 257 and 258?"* guessed Clara.

"Well, we'll have to find a Bible from his era to read because the page numbers will surely have changed since his day?" I guessed.

"Robert is also telling me that in his day the grass was more plentiful here, the ground was more even, and the view of the surrounding countryside was better," continued Clara. *"And when he sat down he didn't cross his legs like you do Lucy, but rested his Bible on his knees."*

"Maybe you need to preserve your energy Lucy," I interjected. "Crossing your arms and legs is supposed to stop energy loss."

Clara continued describing her visions: *"Robert is giving you the gift of a quill pen Lucy. He says you have a good book in you and that you have lots of poetry and songs to write too."*

"You were very descriptive with your writings too Robert; if you don't mind me saying. I really enjoyed reading about your adventures. They were written with such flair and talent," I interjected.

Clara informed me that Robert Kirk appeared very flattered by my comments. However, she then went on to say that Robert then told her that his original manuscript was much better, and more descriptive than the one that went into print. Apparently, according to the information Clara was picking up; anger from his fellow clergymen had resulted in a lot of his original work being deliberately, and systematically destroyed.

Just at that, a local gentleman arrived (one of the living variety); which put an end to our private chat with Robert Kirk and the goblins for another day. We exchanged some small talk with this friendly gent, and then began our descent back downhill into the busy modern world again.

(Grozwald and Co. apparently followed us back to their "detached rock", and then we waved goodbye to them. I don't know what happened to Robert Kirk after we left- No doubt he returned to fairyland to serve out the rest of his "prison-sentence".)

CH13 Alone and Misunderstood 27.03.10

I should have been overjoyed at the thought of another adventure in Aberfoyle with the girls, but for some unknown reason, I felt low in mood today. The weather didn't help much either: it was a grey overcast day and the threat of rain was constantly with us.

I sat in gloomy silence, while as usual, Lucy did all the talking: "I feel great today!" she chirped. "On a scale of one to ten; I feel almost on a maximum of ten!"

Please forgive me, but Lucy's upbeat, jovial mood only seemed to make me feel worse, and as soon as the car stopped in Aberfoyle, I jumped out and ran away from the girls into the nearest shop, ignoring their cries as to where I was going. I pretended to browse at the items for sale but I really just wanted to be alone with my thoughts.

After a while, my mobile phone bleeped: It was a message from the girls inviting me to join them for a hot chocolate in the wee café across the road. I gave myself a shake and quietly scolded myself for being so ignorant, allowing my emotions to take such a firm grip of me.

Buttoning up my coat and straightening my back, I crossed the road and entered the café with my head held high.

"What's wrong with you?" they both asked; with genuine concern. "Sit down there, we got you a mocha and a sticky bun," Lucy insisted.

I sat with my hands clasped tightly around my hot drink, taking an occasional sip. The girls sat silently, giving me my space; which was much appreciated. After what seemed like an age, I forced myself to speak:

"I just feel so "Alone and Misunderstood". I don't know what it is; maybe it's this place, maybe I'm tuning into Robert Kirk?"

Lucy gave me a gentle squeeze on the shoulder and Clara a sympathetic smile. After a while, the girls' efforts seemed to be having an impact on me: I now felt a wee bit brighter in mood and decided to brave the trip back to "Fairy Hill".

However, as we crossed the old hump-backed bridge, I started talking about issues close to my heart. It went something like this:

"We live in an increasingly technological world where most people view our planet as a resource rather than a "being", and most people (including me) live life based on "the pleasure principle"; totally disconnected from our planet: Our materialistic attitudes to life have removed us from our true connection; the real reason for living, truly living on Planet Earth.

This planet is a "living being" and WE, in our blind ignorance, are in danger of rendering Mother Earth incapable of supporting life: any life; including our own. I think that's why the fairy kingdom has been forced to reveal itself to us. If they had the choice, they would probably prefer to live alone and undisturbed, but such is the danger posed to their kingdom by humanities' "disposable" attitude towards this planet. How many trash cans will Mother Earth allow us to fill? How many stinking land-fill sites will our planet endure, and our noses have to suffer before we wake up?

Imagine a world where the perfume of a wild flower is engulfed by the putrid smell of toxic garbage? That world could become a future reality if we don't act now.

All you young people out there; this is YOUR planet, and you can't afford to let "Big Businesses" dictate your lives to you. You must insist on reusable products, environmentally-friendly manufacturing processes, and natural food- none of this genetically modified stuff. You young people are this planet's future and you must learn to respect "Her" by reusing and recycling as much as possible: The number of empty plastic bottles, cans, and discarded food packaging I see littering our planet is disgraceful!

WE all need to stop trashing OUR planet, and retake control of OUR own futures. Every single person on this long-suffering planet has to take a portion of the blame for this: WE are all in this together!

Don't be fooled by the gimmicks of some "Big Businesses": they only care about themselves and their massive profits- money they could never spend in a million lifetimes!"

Maybe it was the wrong time to go off on a rant. I apologized and continued walking.

We had now reached Robert's cemetery and, as we were about to enter, Clara captivated us both with another amazing vision:

"I just saw a two wheeled black carriage, drawn by two black horses, rushing past, headed towards "Fairy Hill"."

"Did you catch a glimpse of the driver?" I asked excitedly.

"No, it was going too fast, but I could hear the clatter of horses' hooves and the sound of the horses panting," expanded Clara.

"I wonder if the vision you just had was a ghostly image of the hearse rushing up to "Fairy Hill" to collect Robert Kirk's Body after he had his "fatal heart attack" on the summit?" I guessed.

"It could have been." agreed Lucy. "They would have wanted to collect his body quickly, especially him being such an important figure in the local community."

We composed ourselves and I proceeded to open the cemetery gate, which squealed eerily as we all entered. As we were approaching Robert's Grave, Clara was suddenly arrested by another vision:

"I can see lots of women in this place today, clad in long black dresses, with lace-edged hats, walking slowly and talking to each other. They're walking straight through the wall of that building over there like it doesn't exist!"

"Maybe they're gathered here to mourn Robert's passing?" Lucy guessed. "And maybe that building they're walking right through over there wasn't around in the 17th century?" I concluded.

Lucy then produced a portrait of Robert Kirk that she carried around with her in a purse:

"What a handsome man!" Clara commented. *"No wonder he had all those female admirers at his funeral."*

Lucy nodded in agreement, but her eyes seemed vague and focused elsewhere. There was a heavy and oppressive atmosphere in the cemetery today and even Lucy was eager to leave the place as quickly as she could.

We desperately needed something, or someone, to brighten up the atmosphere and we certainly got it when we eventually arrived at "Grozwald's Rock":

"Grozwald has been waiting patiently for us," Clara informed us both. *"He's sitting on his rock just now, with legs crossed, tapping his knee. Grozwald says "You take long time!"",* repeated Clara.

"Sorry Grozwald; we were paying our respects at Robert Kirk's Grave," I replied, feeling rather silly as I spoke to "The Rock".

Lucy stood there giggling at how stupid I must've looked, but I kept a straight face as I didn't want to risk offending the wee goblin again.

Clara then lapsed again into "Grozwaldspeak": *"Like The Lucy*

Outfit- Pink- Looks like pixie." (Lucy was dressed in a pink waterproof coat, pink Wellingtons, and a blue pointed woolly hat: Indeed, she did look like a giant multi-coloured pixie.)

Suddenly, a robin appeared in the trees above us so Lucy ceremoniously opened her box of bird seed and began sowing it around "The Rock". *"Grozwald just said: "Thanks for shower!""* Clara informed us. *"Now he's having a good old nibble on some of the seeds."*

So we decided to leave the goblin munching on the bird food and continued up "Fairy Hill". It was a straightforward journey and, when we arrived, Lucy immediately spread out her "Peace Flag" at the foot of "Fairy Tree", and began ritualistically sewing more seeds.

Clara walked slowly over to "Fairy Tree" and gently laid her hands on its trunk...

"I can see this place as it was in the distant past: Looking down from the top of this hill, I can see for vast distances. In the olden days, there were very few trees around here and people could see for miles around. Scotland was "The Ancient Land". People came from all over the world to worship here." Clara then suddenly

changed the subject... *""Fairy Tree" is now showering us all with golden droplets... Wait... "Fairy Tree" informs me Adrian that you have an "attachment" between your shoulder blades just now."*

"What does an "attachment" mean?" I enquired with a worried voice.

"A "negative entity" became "attracted" to you when you were walking in another woodland," replied Clara (I'd read somewhere once that the human "aura" acts as a "force field"; and protects us from "unwanted entities" attaching themselves to us but, apparently, there is a weak area around our shoulder blades known as "The Linden Points"; and they are susceptible to attack from "unwanted entities"- I don't know why this is.)

Sure enough, in the past, I had wandered regularly in the woods below Clackmannan Tower in Alloa, and was deeply upset when I came across living fir trees that had been deliberately set on fire by some thoughtless person, or persons. TREES ARE LIVING BEINGS: EVERYONE NEEDS TO UNDERSTAND THAT- AND THEY FEEL PAIN JUST LIKE YOU AND I! Anyway, I'm not ashamed to admit it: I used to hug the trees that had been burnt badly and try to help sooth their pain and fear. However, one day when I was playing tennis, I felt this tugging sensation between my shoulder blades. I just thought I'd pulled a muscle or something, but apparently not so. I stood there in silence, amazed that "Fairy Tree" knew so much about me and my adventures. Intuitively, I sent forgiveness to the unfortunate "entity" that was "attached" to my back, and meanwhile, Lucy draped "The Peace Flag" around my shoulders: "Time for some healing," Lucy said in a calm, soothing voice, and began working her "magic" on me.

After about 15 minutes of Lucy's "laying on of hands"; which felt like a "red hot furnace" on my back, Clara suddenly broke the silence...

"The "Fairy Tree" informs me that the "entity" that was "attached" to your back has now left."

Soon afterwards, Clara collapsed in a heap onto an old tree stump; looking drained.

"Is everything okay Clara?" Lucy and I asked.

"I'm fine... It's just that... sometimes... dealing with other "entities" can be exhausting; and I felt as if I needed a rest... Oh come on... Not now!" groaned Clara.

"What's up?" Lucy asked.

"Grozwald saw me sitting down and jumped at the chance to approach me at eye level. He came up really close but he meant me no harm. It was strange seeing him up close like that: His eyes were dark and shining, and I could see his skin; sleek and smooth. He had one hand supporting an elbow, and he was tapping his chin with the finger of his other hand, saying:

"YOU'RE NOT MAD- YOU'RE NOT MAD-
SOON EVERYONE WILL SEE."

CH14 FREEDOM! 27.05.10

"Wesak" is a very special day for Buddhists and falls on the full moon of May, every year.

In Buddhist countries all over the world there are colourful festivals on this special day. People clean and decorate their houses, and paper lanterns are lit everywhere. Offerings of food, candles, and flowers are made to the Buddhist Monks in their highly decorative and ornate temples. Lots of prayers and chanting can be heard everywhere as the people thank Buddha for his life and teachings.

"Bathing the Buddha" is a ritual carried out by Buddhists on Wesak and, as water is poured over an effigy of Buddha's shoulders, it symbolizes the purification of the mind from greed, hatred, and ignorance.

But why had we all been asked to come back to Aberfoyle on "Wesak"?

None of us knew the importance of this special day at the time of asking.

Lucy had since got married to her boyfriend, and as for poor

Clara; she was studying furiously for her exams, and had to have her work submitted the following day.

Clara looked absolutely exhausted when she met up with us both in Falkirk. I could tell by the look on her face that she just didn't want to be here. However, I'd stressed the importance of "Wesak" to her, time and time again, and she didn't let us down (Clara, you're a champ for turning up!)

"We can't forget the strawberries!" I reminded the girls as we headed out of Falkirk; so we stopped off at the local supermarket and Clara emerged with two containers of the most gorgeous strawberries I'd ever seen! They were massive in comparison to the normal ones we bought, and they were a deep crimson red.

"Where do these come from?" I asked, my mouth watering: "It says; "Country of origin U.S.A."- Can I try one?"

"Go on then," the girls permitted. I popped one into my mouth and they didn't disappoint. They had the strongest strawberry flavour I'd ever tasted and were extremely juicy and sweet. The girls couldn't resist either and we all agreed that they were absolutely gorgeous.

"These strawberries are so befitting for such an important

day," I announced with gusto.

Lucy nodded her head in agreement but poor old Clara was sitting in the back of Lucy's car in her own wee world; with mountains of homework for college, her face etched with worry lines. I felt guilty by comparison; relaxing in the passenger seat reading a book- but what could I do?

It was late afternoon by now and it had been a lovely day. However, a mass of grey cloud had suddenly descended over Falkirk and, as we were joining the M9 dual carriageway, we were peppered by a sudden burst of hailstones. They sounded like popcorn seeds being poured into a bowl as they bounced off the roof of Lucy's car. However, it was a short sharp blast; and soon the clouds soon parted again to reveal a bright blue sky.

"Let's hope it's blue skies from now on," I cried; uttering a silent prayer of hope to back up my wish.

We were still at least ten miles from Aberfoyle when the girls started with their phantom symptoms:

"I have a pain in my right chest area," Lucy suddenly groaned.

Clara began describing similar "pains", except hers were affecting her left side rather than her right. While I was hurriedly scribbling all this stuff down, Clara suddenly announced she'd just heard a voice shouting "FREEDOM"!

As I was jotting this down, I remembered the famous words uttered in the "Braveheart" film: "You will never take away our FREEDOM!" William Wallace had presumably never had an encounter with fairies though, nor eaten their forbidden food, I assumed.

Furiously scribbling away, the girls came out with another barrage of "symptoms" which I was desperate to capture on paper:

Lucy: "I've got a pain in my back and stomach."

Clara: *"That's funny, I've got a pain in my stomach and my feet are cold, but the rest of my body is lovely and warm!"*

Lucy: "I feel a tickling sensation in my left kidney area."

Clara: *"So do I- Do you think it's Robert playing games with us?"*

Clara: *"I now feel pressure on my chest."*

We were still several miles from our destination when Lucy suddenly began belching: "Burrp... It's so awkward driving a car... Burrrrrp... when you're full of wind like this."

"The energies must be strong today. I've never known you to

start burping so soon," I said, glad to get a word in edgeways!

"Oh they are Adrian." interjected Clara. *"You wouldn't believe it! The trees are glowing green: there's a luminescence about them, and their "auras" are much stronger today, stretching out much further than usual."*

Her words were poetry to my ears. How the gift of "second sight" could enhance the descriptive beauty of the world around us. Imagine the poetry and paintings that would be available today if we could all see the world like Clara does?

As we were approaching Aberfoyle, I could see a huge ominous dark cloud hanging over the village:

"I do so hope we don't get soaked later," I said mournfully, pointing up at the clouds (Aberfoyle lies in a valley surrounded by hills; and is prone to cloud build up, which explains our previous "drowned rat" experiences on the top of "Fairy Hill".)

Lucy then began sharing some more bodily sensations with us both: "I now have a lovely feeling in my chest and heart area just now- It's a feeling of awareness."

What a pleasant surprise, I thought. Normally, I'm frantically searching for the heart monitor when Lucy describes her experiences, but for once, I could sit back and relax!

Clara then lifted her head from her intense studies and began engaging her second sight:

"I can see Robert Kirk standing, holding a small Bible between both hands while praying. There are two shiny black ribbons hanging down from either side of his Bible: He looks like he's waiting in anticipation for something."

She then peered out of the back seat window towards "Fairy Hill": "I can see a wonderful golden green glow around "Fairy Hill": It's rising at least two metres above the hill, and the whole area is vibrant and buzzing just now. Everything seems so alive!"

Even I could see how lush the countryside was today. The woodland surrounding Aberfoyle was thickly carpeted with bluebells on this fine day.

"Burrrp... Burrp... Burrrp... Pixies are supposed to... Burrp... use the bluebells as hats," belched Lucy.

We finally arrived at Aberfoyle, and I was surprised at how empty the place was for such an important day. Central Scotland obviously didn't have a large Buddhist population, I assumed. We'd by now exited Lucy's car and were heading towards the hump-backed bridge when Lucy suddenly turned back towards her car, much to the irritation of Clara who was on a strict time schedule.

"Where are you off to now?" asked an uncharacteristically impatient Clara.

"I'm so sorry Clara, I know you're struggling for time, but I suddenly had the urge to go back for my shawl which is in the back of the car.

All the while, a giant black cloud hung ominously above us all, and Clara shouted after Lucy to fetch some waterproofs from the back of the car. Clara returned with some bright pink waterproofs which Clara pulled on. I understandably refused, and would rather risk a good soaking instead.

However, by the time we'd crossed the old bridge, the sun had broken through the cloud cover and we were all feeling more positive now. Everything then just suddenly came to life. The birds were singing and the air was filled with the perfume of wild flowers.

As we walked past the modern housing scheme on our right, a small girl was playing with her scooter, accompanied by her pet dog: both of them enjoying the fine sunshine.

After a while, the kune kune pigs came into full view. They were out in full force today and I parted with a couple of the king size American strawberries. They must have thought it was their birthdays by the look on their piggy faces as they gorged on the succulent fruit. I could sense they were sniffing for more but I had to leave them frustrated.

Eventually, we arrived at the cemetery and, on entering, I had to blink twice: I couldn't believe my eyes! It was as if someone had suddenly added colour to a black and white sketch book: Wild flowers were growing in abundance and the old tree behind the wall was thick with foliage. The place was literally buzzing with the sound of pollinating insects.

"Let's go over to Robert's Grave: I need to write out some wishes on the cotton flags I've made," insisted Lucy. Then she rushed off ahead, acutely aware of Clara's precious time. When Clara and I caught up with her she was sitting on Robert's Tombstone, surrounded by a myriad of wild flowers, furiously writing out wish after wish on her home-made cotton flags: "Here folks, you have a couple each and make your own wishes," Lucy insisted. It was difficult writing on the cotton with ballpoint pens but Clara and I eventually managed.

"This place has a huge energy today!" announced Clara, as she wrestled with ballpoint on cotton.

"Yes it does," I agreed, emphatically. We sat for a while soaking up the sun: "Treeheads" in full bloom!

It was the girls that left the cemetery first. I lingered around for a while trying to sketch the tombstone with the goblin carving on it, but eventually I gave up, deciding a photograph would be an easier option. By the time I left the cemetery the girls were nowhere to be seen, so I raced up the path towards "Fairy Hill" in hot pursuit, passing the old cottage which was now framed in a blanket of wild flowers; looking all the world like a painting on an old biscuit tin. In the distance I spied the girls; they were approaching "Grozwald's Rock", and I'd just about caught up with them when I suddenly stopped dead in my tracks, halted by a tuneful melody coming from the branches of a tree directly above my head. I looked up to see a tiny bird; its breast heaving in and out, like a bagpipe, producing a song which was a hundred times bigger than its size.

Finally, we all arrived at "Grozwald's Rock" as "Treeheads Together", albeit with me puffing and panting like an old man!

"Can you see him?" I asked Clara.

"Yes, he's there," she replied. *"In fact, the whole family is here today: Grozwald, Gorlinda and the three kids. Oh, how the kids have grown, and their hair is longer now. The kids are in the middle, Gorlinda is on the left, and Grozwald is on the right, in the foreground, slapping the rock in anticipation: "Well then, say hello!" he's asking impatiently."*

"Hello Grozwald, fancy a strawberry- they're U.S.A," I confirmed.

""What's wrong with Scottish Strawberries? They're U.S.A- Get them out of here!" he's telling me," replied Clara. *"Now he's off, and his wife and kids have followed him into the woods,"* Clara informed me.

"Doesn't know what he's missing, the ungrateful goblin!" I retorted, popping one of the succulent fruits into my mouth.

So Grozwald and his family were off, and there was no need to hang around, so we all continued through "The Fairy Trail" via the route that Robert used to take. *As we were sauntering up that sacred path, soaking up the wonderful scenery, Clara suddenly got a vision of a "Shining Buddha".*

The woodland was indeed a "fairyland" to behold on this fine day; carpeted with wild flowers, and filled to the brim with birds and insects, feeding off nature's wonderful bounty. The combined perfumes exuding from the fresh pine cones and flowers were intoxicating. The black cloud above us had thankfully come to nothing and, for the first time in ages, Aberfoyle was dry!

On approaching a rocky incline in the path, Clara turned around suddenly to face us both...

"The image of a wolf just appeared across the path in front of me just now. They must have lived long ago in these woods," she surmised.

"I'm all for protecting wildlife but, I must admit, I wouldn't fancy strolling through here if I knew there were packs of wolves roaming around," I added. The girls nodded in agreement.

We continued up the path and, as we went, I could see lots of black slugs dotting the pathway, and pre-warned the girls in case they accidentally squashed them. However, we'd hardly gone as far as "a slug on an electric scooter" when Clara stopped us again:

"The trees are raining down large golden droplets onto us all just now; much larger than on previous visits- such is the energy today!"

Lucy and I listened in amazement and I could picture, in my mind's eye, large globules of a golden "honey-like" substance dripping down on me and permeating my skin, seeping into my body; healing me from within. (Maybe that's why a lot of the honey we eat is that wonderful golden colour; because it comes from trees and plants- and has that healing power. Honey is used in modern medicine to heal wounds, isn't it?)

We arrived at another rocky outcrop, and Clara had another experience:

"I can feel an "energy vortex" here... Wait there's a sound; much like a peacock would make... Aaaaaah," she burbled; as she tried to imitate the call.

"The sound of the peacock is supposed to be a healing sound," Lucy informed us both. As you can imagine, the journey was taking longer than usual as Clara seemed to be detecting so much more today. As we were slowly progressing uphill, the slugs lay dotted around like silent black markers. Just before we reached the summit, the distant barking of dogs could be heard again, but they sounded just like common household pets to me.

Eventually though, we were now standing below "Fairy Tree", having arrived slightly ahead of the slugs- but not by much!

"Just as we arrived here, we were greeted by a "Fanfare Welcome"; a myriad of horns and drums!" Clara gasped.

"I take it everyone's glad to see us then?" Lucy surmised; mirroring my own thoughts exactly.

"I wonder what the big occasion is?" I enquired; full of anticipation and wonderment.

Lucy then rushed towards "Fairy Tree" to examine the gifts and wishes: "Oh look!" she exclaimed in excitement. "There are all sorts of fairy ornaments here; and what do you think of that beautiful silver butterfly ornament?" she squealed.

Clara seemed to share in Lucy's excitement, but I found it hard to get enthusiastic over ornaments. I gave a polite, gentle smile in Lucy's direction.

Lucy then began rhyming off the wishes pinned to "Fairy Tree", and then my ears began to prick up:

""Dear fairies, I wish for a pet wolf"... Maybe that's what you saw earlier Clara," she joked. "There's another: "Please don't let the ash cloud from the volcano affect our holiday","" and Lucy finished off with a more realistic wish: a wish for a pet dog.

While I was silently wishing for a silver "Aston Martin"; Clara interrupted my daydream with another of her amazing visions:

"We're being watched by hundreds of pairs of eyes from the bushes just now."

Lucy and I had no reason to disbelieve her, and I didn't find the thought intimidating in the least, as we had no reason to fear the fairy folk in any way. As I stood there peering into the bushes, trying to see one pair of eyes at least, Clara turned towards me, continuing to describe the invisible world around us all:

"Grozwald is standing beside you just now. He must feel more at home with your male energy."

Now this I could feel! "Is he standing to my right?" I asked, judging by an unusual sensation in my right leg.

"That's exactly where he is!" smiled Clara, with an air of self-satisfaction that my bodily sensations were coinciding with her visions.

Spurred on; Clara suddenly accelerated into a torrent of visions: *"There are two beautifully dressed figures standing over there, arm in arm, smiling at us both: I think it's "The King and Queen of fairyland". They both have what looks like crowns on their heads."*

However, Clara was then interrupted by a tirade of belching from Lucy, who seemed to be responding to the sudden energy changes taking place around her. I'm sure "His and Her Majesty" understood why, and weren't offended in any way by Lucy's "belly burps". Lucy then took her leave and disappeared with the "wish flags"; intending to pin them around "The Fairy Circle".

"Can you see fairies yet?- Can you see fairies yet?- Look at dapple- Look at dapple," blurted out Clara in the finest "Grozwaldspeak". She then went on to explain herself: *"Grozwald is asking you if you can see any fairies yet Adrian? He does like to repeat himself; doesn't he?"* smiled Clara.

Anyway, I did as the wee goblin fellow had asked; and stared with half-shut eyes on the dapple effect made by the sunlight as it filtered through the trees onto the wild grass and bushes, but for the life of me, I couldn't see a thing (Sorry to disappoint you Grozwald).

"When you relax- You see them- Then you see me!" Grozwald said; speaking through Clara.

The wee goblin was probably right: maybe I was trying too hard. I could still feel a strange sensation in front of my right leg though: "Is Grozwald still standing in front of my right leg?" I asked Clara.

"Indeed he is!" replied Clara, then she returned to her familiar "Grozwaldspeak": *"The Big Energy comes- The Big Energy comes."*

Soon afterwards, Lucy appeared from behind "Fairy Tree":

"I've just pinned my wish flag to the tree," she informed us both...

"Sshh... Please be quiet everyone!" interrupted Clara; so obviously connected to another dimension:

"I can hear the most beautiful music just now... That's the only way I can describe it. We haven't anything in our world to compare to it! I can hear gentle chanting prayer song... the voices are so soft... "Ah La La La La"," sang Clara; trying to imitate what she was hearing. *"I can't even come close to imitating it... it sounds like women singing... there's a slow rhythmical build up, an eventual crescendo, then it tapers off. They seem to be merging their voices with the ebb and flow of the wind... It's mesmerizing!"*

"Well, I know you're a very gifted mezzo soprano singer Clara;

because I've heard you, so if it's way beyond anything you could achieve, it must be fantastic!" I guessed.

"Thanks for the compliment Adrian, but honestly, it's probably the most beautiful music I've ever heard!" admitted a humble Clara.

Lucy was visibly intrigued for a moment, but being her usual independent self, she did her own thing; and suddenly collapsed down onto the ground, her back facing "Fairy Tree", with both her legs crossed. She then proceeded to open one of the packs of strawberries, popping a large juicy specimen into her mouth, her eyes brightening up as she savoured the intense flavor: "Excuse me", she said, as she wiped the juice from the side of her mouth. Please everyone, have a strawberry, they're delicious!"

Clara reluctantly took one as I knew she wasn't keen on strawberries, but even she had to admit they were exceptionally good. As for me, I didn't need to be asked twice and initially went for the biggest, reddest, and juiciest strawberry I could find. Then I thought of the elf kids, and decided to leave the best ones for them- I had my chocolate, didn't I?

As Lucy was sitting munching on the berries; a pine cone suddenly fell from "Fairy Tree" and bounced off the top of her head-a direct hit: "Ooww!" she squealed.

"That's what you get for guzzling the elf kids strawberries", I joked. We all laughed, then Lucy handed us some more cotton flags to write more wishes on.

As I was pinning our flags onto the bark of "Fairy Tree", I could see by the look on Clara's face that she was tuning into something amazing:

"I can hear them all chanting a prayer just now: there are male and female voices; and they seem to be chanting in time with the wind. As the breeze picks up; the chants get louder and louder and, as the wind fades, they become quieter and quieter... Now they're chanting "FREEDOM FREEDOM" faster and faster!"

"Lucy... Robert Kirk has now "merged" with you: His face and body are now "superimposed" over yours: You never sat like this: That's the way he used to sit; with legs and arms crossed. He's now "transmitting" his thoughts towards you. Only you can give him his "FREEDOM"... Only You!"

"Why me? What can I possibly do?" cried Lucy; visibly overwhelmed by the burden that had suddenly been placed on her shoulders.

"YOU ARE "THE WIFE"! YOU ARE "THE WIFE"! ONLY YOU CAN GIVE ME MY FREEDOM!" insisted Robert.

"What does he mean?" wailed a helpless Lucy... "Yes, I'm a "wife" now because I've recently married- but what can I do that the rest of you can't?"

Lucy sat by "Fairy Tree", visibly perplexed for a moment- Then came a flood of tears: "That's it... That explains everything: I've been obsessed with this man, wanting to visit his grave all the time, becoming so upset if my flowers went missing from his graveside. I even carried about his portrait in my purse! I always felt a strong bond with him... I would stare mournfully at his portrait for ages. What does it all mean? By this time the tears were streaming down Lucy's face. After a while, she turned to Clara; speaking in a soft, gentle voice:

"Please tell Robert that I will do whatever it takes to secure his release."

"JUST SAY IT! JUST SAY IT! The energies are at their strongest just now: there's no time to waste... JUST SAY IT!" demanded Clara.

Lucy composed herself briefly and the following words just appeared on her lips:

"Robert, my dear Robert, I am now releasing you from your bondage... You now have your "FREEDOM"!" Lucy uttered these words as if in a trance, and then slumped back against "Fairy Tree".

Clara continued with her commentary:

"I can see a huge "band of gold" around you just now Lucy: it's expanding fast and is so beautiful! Now there's a huge "golden orb" at your feet... "THANK YOU... THANK YOU!" Robert is shouting:

"I'M FREE... FREE AT LAST!" He is beside himself with joy!"

Had this been the main reason for our "calling" to Aberfoyle: the releasing of Robert Kirk from his years of imprisonment in the fairy realms; or were there other reasons as well?

Maybe the elves would treat us all to another adventure in the future and give us some more insights into their wonderful lives. We could only hope and pray.

I walked back down "Fairy Hill", slowly, with tears in my eyes. Why had I been involved in such an important event? I certainly wasn't a saint- anyone who knows me will tell you that. One thing I did know was that I would have to take a lot of "flak" in the future for putting this stuff down on paper, but hey, I was prepared to do it!

Clara continued to share more sacred information with me as she walked behind me:

"The planets are in alignment just now; which accounted for the extra energy... It had to be "THE WIFE", and it needed to be "THE POWER OF THREE"."

I continued to scribble frantically in my note pad; away in a world of my own. The tears continued flowing down my cheeks. This had been the most momentous time of my life. I was so blessed to have been one of "The Treeheads".

When I did eventually come to my senses, however, I turned round to check on the progress of the girls: Lucy was nowhere to be seen but Clara was about ten metres behind me; and closing in fast...

"As you turned round to face me Adrian, Grozwald jumped off your right shoulder: He was perched on your shoulder; trying to read what you were writing in your note pad," Clara informed me; exposing the goblin's antics.

"Oh, was he now?" I laughed. "What a nosey little goblin!" My tears of wonderment had now become tears of laughter.

"Grozwald is now calling me a "Tell-Tale- Tell-Tale" because I

gave his game away," smirked Clara. *"He was muttering under his breath as he wandered off."*

Laughing together at the cheeky wee goblin's huffy behaviour, Clara and I continued the rest of the journey down "Fairy Hill", walking abreast.

"You know something Clara: I've spent the last twenty odd years reading lots of books on ghosts and stuff, while all my friends and family listened to music or watched television. Sometimes my Dad would pick up one of my books and say: "What nonsense are you reading today son?" I'm not criticizing my Dad, he's a good sort, and an avid reader of history, but I think he labeled the stuff I read as "fiction". When I first met you and discovered that you were actually seeing all the stuff I had only read about: that's when I knew it had all been worthwhile," I sighed, contentedly.

"All I can say is that all those years you've spent reading your "nonsense" hasn't been in vain," smiled Clara... then she suddenly stopped dead in her tracks:

"Can you hear church bells ringing just now?" she asked.

"All I can hear is the silence of a fading spring day," I answered poetically. "Maybe it's Robert thanking us all for releasing him from captivity?" I suggested... "Oh, by the way, where is the elusive Lucy?"

"I don't know," replied a worried Clara. *"I hope she's on her way back to the car because I've got a very tight schedule ahead of me."*

The setting sun was now filtering through the undergrowth; illuminating "Grozwald's Rock" as we passed. I waved in the direction I guessed Grozwald and his family might have been standing just now. *Clara reassured me that they'd all waved back.*

As we both walked back to the car, it suddenly dawned on me that this was the closing chapter: Robert finally had his "FREEDOM."

So much had rested on this day for poor Robert Kirk, and none of us had realized quite how important "Wesak" would be. The poor Reverend must have been sweating in his "dog collar"; praying that we'd all show up.

We both finally arrived at Lucy's car to find her sitting in the driver's seat, waiting patiently for us both: "Where have you been?" she quizzed. "I've been waiting here for at least twenty minutes!"

Another "time-slip" in fairyland', I thought. I'd read stories of people who had spent what they thought was a few days with the fairies, and returned to the human kingdom to find that MONTHS, or even YEARS had passed! Maybe Robert's three centuries trapped in fairyland had only felt like a couple of weeks- at least I hoped it had for his sake!

Will Robert come back in a later book and tell us all about his 300 year adventure in fairyland- who knows?

I just hope he's reunited with his loved ones just now, and in future he might think twice before munching on a "fairy cake"; no matter how mouth-watering it might appear!

THE END

VISIONS and IMPRESSIONS

Clara's visions of a bygone era

19.03.10

"I was walking along an old, slate grey, cobbled road: I recognized it as Aberfoyle; but in the olden days. There were only a few old grey stone cottages dotted about here and there, and no fir trees anywhere- apart from the occasional oak.

In my vision; I'd crossed a tiny bridge across the river, and was walking down an old lane towards a graveyard. The place was very sparsely populated and I could see for miles around. I walked past an old church and I could see a young man standing, smiling at me.

As I got closer, I seemed to recognize him to speak to but didn't seem to know him that well. He was slender in build, appeared to be in his twenties, and was wearing dark brown clothes; with a stiff collar, folded at the neck. Over his clothes he had on a tailored jacket and was sporting a thin jaw beard. He had a kindly face and smiled as I walked past. I had a feeling that I had just walked past a youthful Robert Kirk!"

Impressions of Robert Kirk

Clara: *"I got a vision of Robert writing with a quill pen, in a small dark room, lit only by candlelight. I got the distinct impression he wasn't in good physical health when he was writing and could feel myself wanting to cough, as if suffering from a chronic chest complaint. Then I could see, in my "mind's eye", Robert standing in the middle of a group of very angry clerics; their faces were purple with rage. I felt that Robert had either shown them his writings about the fairies, or they had discovered them at his house. Whatever had happened, poor Robert was standing there totally alone; trying to defend himself against the fury of "The Presbyterian Establishment" at that time: "Alone and Misunderstood".*

Latest Developments 17.10.14

It's been five long years since I first put pen to paper; sharing Clara's amazing, and often hilarious accounts of the antics of Grozwald the goblin. I have since written another two "Treeheads" books which are available on "Kindle".

Up until several months ago, I had no other option but to rely on Clara's sensitive vision and hearing; trusting wholeheartedly that she was genuinely tuning into the fascinating world of fairy- that was until I saw Grozwald myself for the first time!

Clara and I visited Aberfoyle on the day after Summer Solstice (2014); and it was on that calm, bright afternoon that I was fortunate enough to set eyes on Grozwald for the first time: All I can say is that it was a strange experience: Grozwald appeared as a silhouette: I could see his head shape: He had a large skull which tapered to a thin jawline. His eyes were very large and, in sharp contrast, he had a very small mouth. His ears were long and pointed, and stretched over the top of his head: He was not unlike a cat to look at and Grozwald explained that some people; who could see the goblins, often mistook them for domestic cats due to their size and appearance. He was sitting on an old barrow, and I could see his full figure: He was about the same size as a largish teddy bear. Clara took a photograph at the same time as I saw him; and the camera picked up a "distortion" which matched exactly the shape of the small figure I saw on that special day with my own eyes.

Before I go, I also have another important development to share with you all: Rosalie visited Aberfoyle a few weeks later, and took another photograph; which I think is the most conclusive to date: This photograph reveals a goblin-type face which I have reproduced on the back cover of the book. I have since shown this photograph to Grozwald and he claims that the face is none other than his mischievous cousin "Thorak". Grozwald told me that this "Thorak" character is very unfriendly, and often comes down to spy on him. He also informed me that "Thorak" dislikes humans.

Well, whoever or whatever this photograph may be of; it certainly doesn't look very welcoming- does it?

Bye for now,

Adie Bain (17th of October, 2014)